THE CLIFF

The Cli

by Donald Chaput

ff

America's First Great Copper Mine

Sequoia Press / Publishers
Kalamazoo, Michigan / 1971

To Toni, Ben, and Ed

To-day the Cliff Mine has no rival in this region nor in the world.

Horace Greeley, New York Tribune, 1847

CONTENTS

This is the story of the Pittsburgh & Boston Copper Mining Company and their most famous property, the Cliff Mine of Lake Superior. The Cliff was the first successful copper mine in the Americas, and over the decades she developed characteristics that would be copied on other mining frontiers. Rather than try to concentrate on only mining history, I have attempted to show how the mining communities developed, what the pattern was for shipping and marketing of the metal, and what impact the Lake Superior copper fields had on the national and international trade networks. I may have attempted too much, but I hope that the reader will at least have a fair understanding of the many, varied aspects of life in a frontier mining economy.

At one point in the book I emphatically state that French Canadians did not take to work in the mines; in fact, they did what they could to avoid such employment. I am of French-Canadian descent, so one may logically wonder at the forces that interested me in mining history. Although they avoided mining, the *Canadiens* did flock to the mining frontier and worked in and near villages for the mining companies. The *Canadien* specialty was lumbering, and there was a score of occupations that called for various wood skills. Timber for the mines, lumber for the homes and buildings, fuel for the engines and stoves—these were just a few of the "wood" needs of the mines. On my father's side, the first ancestor on the mining frontier supplied logs to several smelters; some of my mother's first memories are of her early years at the Ojibway Mine, where her father was employed as a surface hand. My father worked for the great Calumet & Hecla firm for over thirty years, but in true *Canadien* fashion he worked in surface plants, not in the mines.

In the past few years some outstanding mining publications have appeared, and the titles reveal the scope of interest: Katherine A. Harvey, *The Best-Dressed Miners: Life and Labor in the Maryland Coal Region, 1835-1910* (Ithaca: Cornell University Press, 1969); Clark C. Spence, *Mining Engineers & The American West* (New Haven: Yale University Press, 1970); and Howard and Lucille Sloane, *A Pictorial History of American Mining* (New York: Crown Publishers, 1970). This book on the Pittsburgh & Boston Company focuses on a specific mine in a few decades before and after the Civil War. I hope that in some respects the detailed history of one mine will make some contribution to mining and frontier history and supplement what some of the above studies do so well in a broader sense.

My wife Toni has been with this project since I picked up my first Pittsburgh & Boston annual report; her editing has repaired much of my enthusiastic writing. My parents have done much to encourage my interest in Lake Superior history, as has my friend Earl Gagnon of the Houghton *Daily Mining Gazette*. The staff of the Michigan Historical Commission in Lansing helped frequently by providing materials from their rich mining collections, as well as in the gathering of illustrations. Harry Kelsey read my manuscript and helped to control my broad generalizations. Jim Schutze helped during several phases of the printing of the book. I also wish to thank the efficient, courteous staff of the Pennsylvania Room in the Carnegie Library, Pittsburgh. The Sequoia Press of Kalamazoo has for many years been one of the Midwest's leading printing firms, and I have been pleased to have their art staff perform so well with such challenging nineteenth century illustrations.

D.C.

Chapter 1:

Background and Discovery

Digging in a copper pit, 3,000 years ago.

IN 1826 WHITE PIGEON, a Chippewa Indian from the Ontonagon River band, knocked at the door of United States Indian Commissioner Thomas McKenney. McKenney was at the western end of Lake Superior with Michigan Territorial Governor Lewis Cass, where they were making a treaty with the Chippewas. White Pigeon was "pining in wretchedness," and McKenney quickly called for an interpreter to question this Indian, an "object of contempt." Before the interpreter arrived, White Pigeon with a "quick but feeble step" disappeared. McKenny soon learned the reason for the misery of that lonely Indian.

In 1820 General Cass, Indian agent Henry R. Schoolcraft, and others had visited the southern shore of Lake Superior to see the famous copper boulder located up the Ontonagon River. At first they could find no Chippewa to guide them to the boulder, because the Indians considered this and all copper deposits sacred. Finally, White Pigeon agreed to take them. He lost his way, a peculiar circumstance indeed for a local Indian guide. His band felt that the gods had caused him to miss the boulder. From that time on a series of misfortunes befell White Pigeon. In McKenney's words, "the game of the forest avoided him; his weapons failed to perform their fatal office." The Ontonagon Chippewa band expelled him, and White Pigeon lived for years on roots and berries, a sad, lonely Indian who had violated tribal law.[1]

This incident points out two remarkable aspects of the Lake Superior frontier. For generations it was common knowledge that there was much copper in the area, and for hundreds of years the Indians did their best to keep the copper sites hidden from a succession of European and New World explorers.

From three to five thousand years ago Indians had come to the Keweenaw Peninsula and Isle Royale to pick up pieces of float copper deposited by various glaciers and to dig and cut other pieces of pure copper from large copper masses. The copper was taken south to villages, where it was made into weapons and ornaments; some of this copper was traded to the Pacific Coast, and other pieces found

White Pigeon.

Lewis Cass, Governor of Michigan Territory.

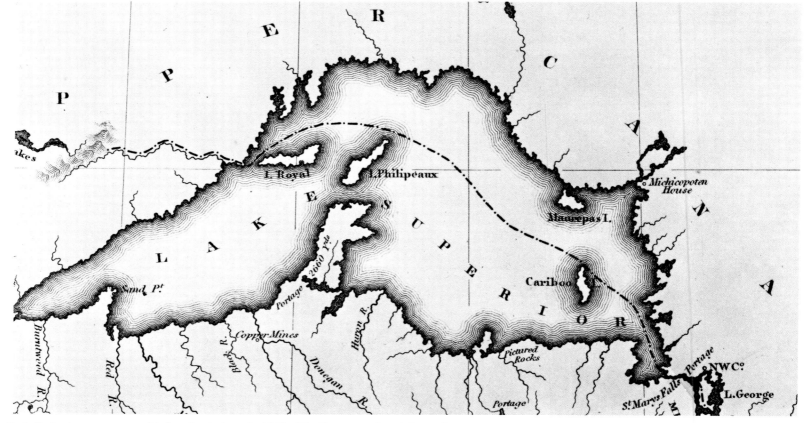

Lake Superior was an unsettled region before the 1840s. The "copper mines" shown here represent Alexander Henry's abortive venture of the previous century.

their way into Aztec lands. However, for several hundred years before the coming of the French, the Indians had for unexplained reasons abandoned the copper workings, and although the local Chippewa and Cree knew of the copper they seldom used it. By this time a complete superstition had surrounded the red metal.[2]

By the mid-1600s the French knew of the copper, largely due to the explorations of Pierre Esprit Radisson. In the *Jesuit Relation* of 1669-1670 Father Claude Dablon related a copper superstition that would be repeated and em-

bellished for decades. Four Indians camped on an island in Lake Superior and used heated pieces of copper to help boil some water. While the men were leaving the island, a supernatural voice boomed: "Who are these robbers carrying off from me my children's cradles and playthings?" The Indians, "stricken with terror," fled the island. Three of them died at once, one returned to give the macabre news to the village, then he also died.[3]

From time to time the French explored and set up experimental mines in the region. The first attempt was by Pierre

Le Sueur in the 1690s. He formed a company in New France and took fifty men to the western end of Lake Superior to seek for and mine copper. Political squabbles in New France hampered his mining authorization. Furthermore, a high official of Montreal seemed to have pegged Le Sueur's interests correctly: "I think the only mines that he seeks in those regions are mines of beaver-skins." Beaver trade was temporarily prohibited at this time, so Le Sueur used his mining as a cover for getting skins.[4]

Louis Denis, known as Sieur de la Ronde, commanded the post at Chequamigon Bay near modern Ashland, Wisconsin, in the 1730s. He explored for copper along the south shore of Lake Superior, sent samples to Paris for testing, and in 1734 began work on deposits along the Ontonagon River in the present state of Michigan. La Ronde had a twenty-five-ton ship built, and by 1739 he had developed a plan for smelting and shipping the copper to Detroit. However, a major Sioux-Chippewa territorial struggle took place in western Lake Superior in the 1740s, ending the only serious French attempt to mine for copper.[5]

The only British effort to work the copper deposits was headed by Alexander Henry in the early 1770s. Earlier, in 1765, the fur trader had stopped at the Ontonagon River and was impressed with the pieces of native float copper. In 1771, near Sault Ste. Marie, he built a forty-ton sloop and went to Ontonagon with a crew of miners, where he built a house, set up the miners for the winter, and returned to the Sault. In early 1772 he sent supplies from the Sault to the Ontonagon camp, but he was disappointed and surprised to see the sloop and the entire crew of miners return in June of that year. Apparently during the winter the men had excavated an adit (horizontal opening) forty feet into the side of a hill, only to have the entire works cave in. The copper finds had been small anyway, so Henry abandoned the mining venture.[6]

The new American regime was so busy trying to expel the British from the area that they found little time for exploring, and only after the War of 1812 did specific knowledge of copper deposits become known. Most of the attention was focused on the famed Ontonagon boulder, a two-ton copper rock some thirty miles up the Ontonagon River. By the mid-1820s Cass, McKenney, Schoolcraft, geologist Douglass Houghton, and others had knocked off specimens of the massive rock. George Porter, soon to become territorial governor of Michigan, visited the site in 1826 and reported on its "masses of pure metal one hundred pounds in weight." Porter wanted to take the boulder back to Detroit, but its bulk and weight made this an impossible task.[7] More ingenious minds would succeed.

When Cass, McKenney, Porter, et al visited the region they were officials examining the land and treating with the Indians. Private individuals had no mineral rights whatsoever on these Indian lands, and it was largely the responsibility of Henry R. Schoolcraft, agent at Mackinac, to keep all non-Indians away from copper deposits. In early 1840, for example, United States Indian Commissioner T. H.

Henry Rowe Schoolcraft.

13

Crawford warned Schoolcraft that a Mr. Ainsley from Upper Canada intended to settle Keweenaw Point "for purposes of getting copper."

Schoolcraft's reply is key to what control existed during this era. He assured Crawford that "full power and means . . . are possessed by this office to prevent any attempt of the Kind." Schoolcraft knew personally hundreds of Indians, and by his marriage to the daughter of a celebrated Chippewa war chief he had contacts with all the tribes of the Lake Superior area. He would at once be informed of any mining activity and "due vigilence will be exercised to prevent any infraction of the laws."[8]

The Indians owned the land, hence also the minerals, but Eastern speculators and industrialists needed more copper, and it would be only a short time before the Indian rights were altered. By the early 1800s Paul Revere and family had developed a modest copper works at Boston, where they refined copper sheets for ship bottoms. Some of the copper was from New Jersey and Virginia, but most of it was imported from England, South America, and Mexico. By 1813 in addition to the Revere works there were two other copper manufactories, the Gunpowder Copper Works near Baltimore and a firm in New York, both limited to production of 100 tons per year, and both serving shipping interests. By the 1830s much of the copper was coming from mines in Connecticut and New Jersey, but the demand for copper sheets, bolts, rods, and spikes was much greater than the supply.[9]

Also by the 1830s brass manufacturing, a combining of copper and zinc, had become highly developed in Connecticut, especially in Waterbury. By the late 1830s buttons, hinges, cabinet hardware, and kitchen utensils were being manufactured from brass, and New Haven County had a near monopoly on domestic brass production. Much of the zinc came from Pennsylvania, but copper was still mostly imported.[10]

The small domestic copper output, before the Michigan mines opened in the 1840s, was scattered over New England, New Jersey, Pennsylvania, and Maryland, and small

Dr. Douglass Houghton

smelteries also existed in some of these states. For some time Vermont was the leading copper-mining state, and the Ely Copper Mine there was the largest in the Union. However, the expanding uses for copper meant that either the manufacturers had to pay the high price for imported copper or find new domestic sources.[11] There was an obvious solution to this problem: the rich copper fields of Lake Superior must be tapped.

By the early 1840s Dr. Douglass Houghton, geologist for the state of Michigan, had made several trips to the Lake Superior country, and his enthusiastic reports were eagerly read and discussed in Detroit and in the East. The copper was there, said the "little doctor," but the land was controlled by the Chippewa Indians. This was taken care of by the Treaty of La Pointe (Wis.), made by Indian Commissioner Robert Stuart, former official with the American Fur Company. The treaty, which went into effect in March of 1843, resulted in the Chippewa cession of roughly all land near present Marquette, Michigan, west to modern Duluth, Minnesota. This massive cession contained the famed Copper Country of northern Michigan, as well as three major iron ranges. The Indians received their usual few dollars and tobacco, and Stuart boasted to his superiors that he had "done in" the half breeds "by excluding the usual allowance." According to Stuart, the Indians were "much pleased with the provisions of the Treaty."[12]

The Keweenaw Peninsula at once attracted prospectors and speculators. General Walter Cunningham was sent from Washington to Lake Superior to open a Mineral Land Agency. Stuart, writing from Detroit, suggested that Cunningham counsel closely with Dr. Houghton regarding the geology of the district, and with Stuart in matters of Indian affairs, "for much will depend of first movements and impressions." Stuart then further greased Cunningham's path by instructing Indian Agent James Ord of Sault Ste. Marie to assist the General in every way, even to send his best interpreter. The interpreter, Eustache Roussain, should "impress on the Indians, that Genl C. has come with full powers from the President, that he is also your

friend and mine, and that they must not only prevent any interruption to his operations, but be ready at all times to do whatever he may require of them."[13] Cunningham established the agency at Copper Harbor on June 18, 1843. Dozens of mining permits were issued, and a week later the settlement consisted of nine tents. Men were there from Boston, New York, and other Eastern cities, but they were in wild, unfamiliar country. "A single man cannot penetrate this country without a hatchet to cut the limbs from the trees," wrote one disgruntled Easterner.[14]

During this period the famous "theft" of the Ontonagon boulder occurred, and the episode demonstrates some typical aspects of frontier ethics. Julius Eldred, a Detroit hardware merchant, heard tales of the brilliant copper mass and decided to make a financial coup: he would get the boulder, take it to Eastern states, and exhibit it for a fee. In 1841 Eldred and an interpreter went to the Ontonagon River, paid the local chiefs $150 for the boulder, went up the river, and placed the boulder on skids.

In the summer of 1842 Jim Paul, a southerner temporarily from Wisconsin, arrived at the Ontonagon River, tried without success to get Chief Plover's cooperation in removing the boulder, and decided to go the site, build a cabin, and squat for the winter.

James Kirk Paul, who almost had the celebrated copper boulder, but who settled for a career as owner of the Deadfall Saloon.

Eldred and crew moving the Ontonagon Copper Boulder.

*Modern Copper Harbor; in the center is Porter's Island, the site
of the Mineral Land Agency.*

In the summer of 1843 Eldred and party arrived on the scene, argued fiercely with Paul, and they were both visited by General Cunningham. Paul then supposedly scared off the General, who later returned with the U. S. Navy, that is, a Navy cutter. Cunningham apparently had received orders from the Secretary of War to get the boulder and send it to Washington. Paul, enraged at this bureaucratic pomposity, drew two Colts and shouted: "I'll shoot the first son-of-a-bitch who touches that there Rock." Finally, Eldred persuaded Paul to sell his "rights of possession" in the rock for $1,800. Paul took the money and promptly built the first saloon in town. Cunningham by then was perplexed and under pressure. He knew that Eldred had a lot of money at stake, so he permitted Eldred to transport the two-ton boulder to Detroit for a temporary exhibition. This was done in October of 1843, and then the boulder was taken to Washington, where after some time it was put on display in the Smithsonian Institution. Congress later awarded Eldred $5,654 for his troubles. The furor created by this boulder marked the first full year of the opening of the copper fields.[15]

Among those who were early attracted to the bonanza news from the copper lands was Curtis Grubb Hussey, a physician-merchant-pork dealer from Pittsburgh. Hussey had moved to the city in 1840, and this was a good location for hearing hot east-west news.

In the summer of 1843 Hussey was visited by a druggist, John Hays of Cleveland, a hunting and fishing friend who was about to journey to Lake Superior to check over some copper land and at the same time regain his health. Hays had read an article in the Pittsburgh press about the new, wild copper frontier, and he was certain that great minerals could be found there. Hussey agreed to pay half of the expenses, plus furnish funds for mining leases. Hays left Pittsburgh on August 17, 1843. He journeyed on the steamer "Chesapeake" to Mackinac, took a canoe to Sault Ste. Marie where he boarded the schooner "Algonquin" for Copper Harbor.[16]

John "Old Blind" Hays, discoverer of the Cliff riches.

Once in the tent city Hays made frequent exploratory trips in the vicinity and kept his ears open for the many copper rumors. One day, while Hays was supposedly standing a few prospectors to some alcohol, a Bostonian named Jim Raymond pounded on the slivered bar and shouted: "I got three of the best god-damned claims on the Keweenaw—pure copper sticking right out of the greenstone on one of them—and I can't raise a cent to take the stuff out. What I need is a partner." Hays poured the man another drink, and within a few minutes he was scribbling an agreement on the back of an old letter that gave Hays and Hussey the option to purchase for $1,000 one-sixth interest in the three claims.[17]

Raymond had apparently received the first three mining permits issued by the government. The first permit was for three miles square, including and surrounding Copper Harbor. The second was for three miles square to the west of Eagle River, and the third was a like quantity to the west of the Eagle River tract.[18]

Hays returned to Pittsburgh and reported the transaction to Hussey, who became enthusiastic. Hussey and Hays signed an agreement on November 13, 1843, and Hussey was to pay for one-sixth of the interest in the Keweenaw district lands; Hays was to get one-fourth of all profits from mining and smelting. However, one-sixth interest in the leases did not seem enough, so Hays spread the copper gospel to Dr. Charles Avery, Thomas Howe, and Dr. William Pettit, all men of means from Pittsburgh. They decided to purchase an additional three-sixths of the interest, which then gave the Pittsburgh group two-thirds control.[19] A few Boston investors, especially Charles Scudder, retained holdings, but Raymond had enough. By 1846 he was operating the Porter Island House, offering some of the finest booze and worst bedding in Copper Harbor.[20]

The Pittsburgh group authorized Hays to explore the properties the following summer. In the spring of 1844 Hays, eight Pennsylvania coal miners, and geologist Alfred Rudolph left Cleveland on the schooner "Swan" for Sault Ste. Marie.[21] There Hays visited with explorer-surveyor

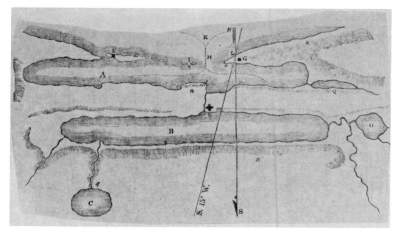

This 1845 map features the Mineral Land Agency (F), Pittsburgh and Boston cabins (G), and Fort Wilkins (E).

C. C. Douglass on June 23. Douglass was amazed because Hays even had along some furnace equipment. "He is sanguine of full success," said Douglass, "& he is a fine intelligent man."[22] From the Sault the Hays group took the "Algonquin" to Copper Harbor.

Of the three permit sites that the Pittsburgh group had obtained, it was obvious why they decided to begin work at Copper Harbor. This was the area of the well-known "green rock" reported by generations of *voyageurs*. Here was a vein colored by silicate and oxide of copper, and the "green" was particularly conspicuous at this site, named soon after as Hays' Point. Before much work could be done here, though, workmen found that the vein re-appeared on the other side of the Harbor as black oxide of copper. This was a near-surface find, and it caused much wild excitement among the Hays party and rivals.[23]

This discovery occurred in late autumn, and by early December mining was begun, two shafts were sunk 40 and 60 feet deep, about 100 feet apart, near Lake Fanny Hooe. Some twenty-six tons of black oxide were taken out, the first known vein found anywhere containing this as the principal ore. The Pittsburgh group felt they had "fair prospects." This was another milestone in American mining and was proudly recalled some years later by Hussey:

> The first regular mining shaft ever attempted in the country was sunk in 1844, under the direction of the present President of this company.[24]

Hussey's visit to Lake Superior in that same year was a weary Odyssey that took him by steamer from Cleveland to Mackinac Island. From there he chartered a safe but uncomfortable Mackinaw boat to Sault Ste. Marie. He had to wait there for three weeks before the only boat on Lake Superior, the "Algonquin," picked up a load of passengers and took them to Copper Harbor. After inspecting the mineral works for a few weeks he took the "Algonquin" back to the Sault, from where he chartered a canoe for Mackinac Island. Hussey was apprehensive about the canoe, which consisted of two Indians with paddles and sail carrying four passengers and assorted trunks.[25]

Daniel "Dad" Brockway, later to be called "Father of the Copper Country," and also later to serve as mining agent for the Cliff Mine, was government blacksmith at the L'Anse Chippewa Indian reservation at this time. He wrote a letter from L'Anse on December 10, 1844, praising the Copper Harbor finds as "richest and most extensive in the world."

> Mr. Hays, the gentleman who discovered the vein and is the agent of a very heavy company in Pittsburgh, Pa. is now here, and on his way to Pittsburgh. He is going through the woods to Green Bay, and is to carry this letter.[26]

Hays also told Brockway that the work was so easy that two men raised 3,300 pounds of oxide in one day, and that the copper yield was 80 per cent. Hays and two Indian guides walked to Wisconsin in ten days, where he took a sleigh and stage to Detroit. While in Detroit Hays showed some specimens to Dr. Houghton, who was much impressed. Hays then went on to Pittsburgh by boat and stage.

The year 1844 also saw the raising of a military post at Copper Harbor, immediately adjacent to the shafts sunk by

A Mackinaw boat, used by Hussey and other early copper explorers.

the Hussey-Hays crew. Michigan congressmen and senators had addressed a memorial to the Secretary of War William Wilkins in March, urging that the army step in to regulate possible Indian troubles, be in charge of any

Indian removal, control a rowdy collection of frontier miners-speculators, and see to it that some authority be established in this wilderness. Indian agent Stuart, too, felt that several companies of troups were needed in the new mineral region "where they may be most effective in detecting whiskey smugglers, and in preventing mischief between the miners and the Indians." Stuart suggested that Ontonagon would be a good site for the fort, but the creation of the Mineral Land Agency at Copper Harbor in 1843 and the wild rumors of copper finds there pretty much convinced the military that Copper Harbor would be better.[27]

The request to Congress was approved, and in May, 1844, Companies A and B of the Fifth Regiment arrived at Copper Harbor and began to build a post, which to nobody's surprise was named Fort Wilkins. The fort was situated on a band of land between Lake Superior and Lake Fanny Hooe, one of the most picturesque military locations in the country. No Indian troubles or massive breakdowns in law and order took place in the vicinity, so that over the years duty at Fort Wilkins was akin to being at a pleasure resort. Yet, when the post was created in 1844 the nation was not quite certain what protection was needed on the mining frontier.[28]

The year 1845 was one of wild speculation on the Keweenaw Peninsula. The mineral agency on Porter's Island opened for business as unusual in mid-June, and soon permits abounded, and the tent settlement grew rapidly. One of the few "non-government" log buildings in the area was the Astor House, a 24′ x 16′, one and one-half story structure run by a jack-of-all-trades half-breed named Francois. John R. St. John visited the Astor House at this time and described the twenty-five-cent dinners (trout, pork-and-beans, bread, coffee, etc.) and the twenty-five-cent sleeping arrangements (on the floor where room was available, on bags of oats or buffalo skins).[29]

Hundreds of permits were issued, some from Porter's Island, others directly from Washington. St. John described the *Pawnees*, a mining type who put "their paws upon the shoulder" of newcomers and whispered about the magic permits they had stuffed in their pockets.[30] By this time around 700 permits had been issued. Naturally, the small mineral agency staff confused some of the locations, and there were many other "irregularities" typical of the frontier. Most of the permit holders were from the Eastern cities of Boston, New York, Baltimore, and Philadelphia, though many of the permits were held by residents of "western" cities like Buffalo, Pittsburgh, Cleveland, Detroit, and Chicago.[31] The number of permits mattered little, for only two concerns were doing any mining. The Pittsburgh and Boston Mining Company, controlled largely by Hussey, Avery, and other Pittsburgh financiers, were working at Copper Harbor, while near Eagle River the Lake Superior Mining Company under Colonel Charles Gratiot was sinking shafts and getting some copper.

Hays spent January and February of 1845 in Pittsburgh, collecting supplies and recruiting men. The partners felt that they had a great find, and Hays was encouraged from all sides. He left Pittsburgh in late February with thirty men and took the difficult land route: Detroit, Chicago, and up through Wisconsin, and reached Copper Harbor on March 21. Two new shafts were sunk, about 500 yards inland, and some black oxide was found. Hays at this time was forty years old, but he had a variety of eye problems. Then, and for the next fifty years, he was often referred to as "Old Blind Hays."[32]

During this time Hays either asked to be relieved because of his health (his story) or he was fired by Dr. William Pettit, "who announced himself as agent of the mine." Hays agreed to go but only if the men got paid their long overdue wages. In the subsequent exchange between two Quakers, Pettit said, "John, thee must take thy men to Pittsburgh and they will be paid." Hays replied: "Then, thee will not get possession of the mine." The miners were ornery, so when Pettit started to walk to the mine the men threatened him with muskets and pistols. "John, would thee shoot?" asked Pettit, whereupon Hays said, "William, I will." This convinced Pettit to pay the men.

Fort Wilkins, a few years after construction.

This entire dialogue rests on the memory of Samuel W. Hill, the king of the profanity-obscenity crew on the mining frontier, and one suspects that Hill told this tale often, roaring at the Quaker inability to utter something stronger than, "John, would thee shoot?"[33]

The diggings at this site were good—the Cornish term "looking kindly" was used to refer to the shafts—but after the 120-foot level the vein was lost. This ended active operations on the Copper Harbor lease. In 1844 and 1845, then, the Pittsburgh group spent over $28,000 on exploring, digging shafts, and so forth, and received only $2,968 from the sale of some copper to the Roxbury works in Boston.[34] Where was the copper bonanza? Not at Copper Harbor.

The mighty Cliff Mine, the first great copper mine in the Western Hemisphere, was first worked in 1845, but its origins are hidden in mining frontier legend. We cannot be sure who discovered this rich lode a few miles from Eagle River, but there are many claimants for the glory. Hays reported that in November of 1844, while he was travelling from Copper Harbor to Eagle River, his Mackinaw boat was blown ashore in a squall, and he and two explorers walked to the Eagle River area, where on November 18, 1844, he discovered the Cliff. Supposedly it was this news that impressed his Pittsburgh associates a few weeks later. The Hays tale is somewhat confirmed by Dad Brockway's letter of December 10, 1844, quoted earlier. Brockway said that Hays reported good mining at Copper Harbor, but "especially one at Eagle River, which has been thoroughly tested, and is beyond a doubt invaluable."[35]

Some later accounts said that Jim Raymond knew of the Cliff deposits and told Hays about them. Many contemporaries reported that the Cliff was discovered by a "Mr. Cheny" and a party of explorers in August of 1845.[36] One later version claimed that "Dr. Rudolph later went to Cliff and located the afterwards famous Cliff Mine."[37]

Some of the legend was enlarged over the years as the Cliff's reputation grew. In 1882 the local Houghton newspaper reported that Walter Cuthbert of Pittsburgh was "dragging out a miserable existence in a hovel." He had apparently made the key discovery at the Cliff, and the stockholders "could well afford to put this man beyond want for the balance of his life." This sad tale does not match the earlier 1880 "AID FOR THE FIRST DISCOVERER OF COPPER ON THE CLIFF MINE." It seems that Edward Hagart was living "in penury" near Mineral Springs, Wisconsin. The *Gazette* publicized a relief fund for the Cliff-finder, and $13.75 "poured in."[38]

Hays was most likely the first to realize the potential of the Cliff location, so the party under Cheny in August of 1845 was most likely there following Hays' directions. The copper vein was first seen on the top of the 200-foot cliff above a branch of the Eagle River. The vein was a few inches wide, containing native copper and specks of silver. Half-way down the cliff the vein stretched to two feet. United States surveyors Charles T. Jackson and J. D. Whitney visited the find a few days later, and Whitney advised clearing away the brush and rubble at the base of the Cliff. A shaft was sunk by some German miners, and they drove an adit seventy feet into the cliff and struck a great mass of pure copper, "a fortunate circumstance . . . to the whole mining interest on Lake Superior." This was the first mass of native copper found in place in the Lake Superior region; all other pieces of pure copper found so far, including the famed Ontonagon boulder, were "float" copper, moved by glacial action.[39] The mining boom was on!

Life on the frontier at this time was raucus. John H. Forster went to the Lake Superior country in April, 1846, and even at Sault Ste. Marie the Indians and half-breeds, male and female, were "leading not very reputable lives." After a seven-day voyage, Forster arrived at Copper Harbor, where he saw several thousand people in the next few months. He described "a lively town of white tents gleaming out of the green groves."

> Card playing, the use of the "flowing bowl," and some good fighting with fist and pistol, were the social amusements of this conglomerate community . . . . It was a common saying that there was no Sunday west of the Sault.

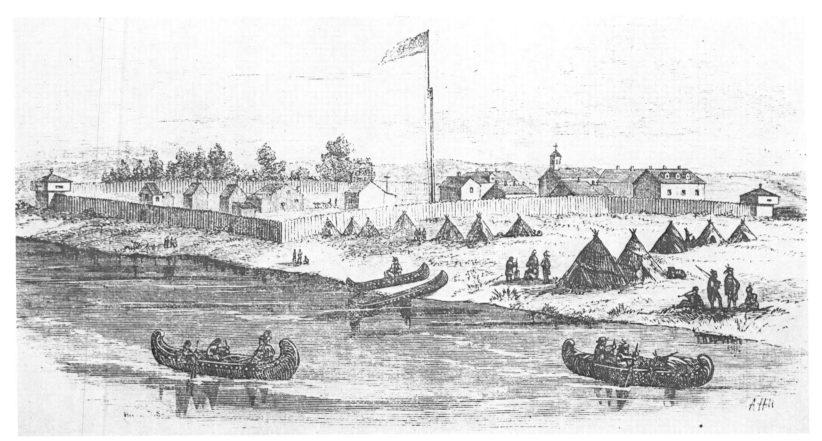

Before the copper rush, the law and order in the Lake Superior country was provided by the garrison at Fort Brady, Sault Ste. Marie.

AMERICA'S FIRST MINING RUSH

By Riggs Sturgis

Years before the rush for California's gold, there was another—for the copper of little Keweenaw Peninsula. And there, ghost towns will live again, new fortunes in red metal will be made.

This romanticized version of the early days conflicts with the pioneer accounts of bad whiskey, fist fights, and crude frontier living.

Copper Harbor was no exception for this type of behavior, as Forster also visited Ontonagon, where he stayed at Jim Paul's Deadfall Saloon: "Chief entertainment, whiskey and tobacco." Forster described the "drinking, carousing, fighting, and all manners of frontier excess. At times the scene is like an arena of infuriated wild beasts."[40]

In 1846 work began in earnest on the Cliff, under the supervision of Captain Edward Jennings, a Cornishman. Two drifts were completed of 125 feet each, and the Cliff was producing copper. For example, the Cliff produced 510,000 pounds of copper in July, and the Lake Superior Company, the only other producer, had a mere 5,165 pounds.

Towards the end of 1846 Jennings was cautiously optimistic. The company claimed credit "of first sending copper from our shores into market in a manufactured state"; the company had contracted with a Boston firm to sheath several ships with sheets of copper. Jennings also reported that in August they had handled 350,000 pounds of copper; some barrels had been shipped, some were ready for shipping, and about 225,000 were being stamped and crushed. Jennings added that the crew had discovered many copper boulders weighing as much as fifty pounds.[41]

This rosy picture began to fade when the figures were tabulated. In 1846 the Company took in $8,870 on sales of copper; they spent $66,128, including the opening of the Cliff Mine, closing of operations at the Copper Harbor works, and a bill for work done at the Roxbury, Mass., smelter.[42]

Up to this time the board of directors of the Pittsburgh and Boston Mining Company, founded in 1844 as a partnership, had assessed its stockholders $110,000 to prosecute the work. In the winter of 1846-47 a board meeting was called in Pittsburgh to make another assessment, but the Boston stockholders would not pay. Dr. Charles Avery, chairman of the board and owner of one-fifth of the shares, was perplexed by the refusal of the Boston group. Avery asked Hussey how deep the mine was and whether or not someone in town could compare the Cliff with Euro-

pean mines. The depth of the Cliff was apparently what frightened the Boston stockholders.

Hussey sent for geologist Alfred Rudolph, who informed Avery that in England some mines didn't "pay" until they were 800 feet deep. Avery then asked his bank treasurer: "Mr. Howe, how much are my credits in this bank?" Avery learned that he had $82,000. He at once pledged $80,000 to the Cliff and directed Hussey to have Captain Jennings "deepen our mine as fast as he can." Thus it was that the Pittsburgh faction, led by an adventurous clergyman, took control of the firm that made deep-shaft mining a profitable reality in North America.[43]

Mining activities in 1847 were somewhat confused and ill-planned, probably a foreseeable situation in such a wilderness. A crew of around 100 miners, agents, carpenters, blacksmiths, and drivers was on hand, and stamping machinery from Boston was being installed. Most of the half-million pounds of copper had been sent to the Roxbury and Revere copper works in Massachusetts. Much silver was found with the pure copper, a happy circumstance that would continue in the copper fields for decades.

Improvements in the mine and village were being rapidly made. The mining agent explained that a *whim* was built for drawing copper from the shaft; the *whim* was pulled by

A whim; primitive but effective.

The stamping works of the Lake Superior Company in 1845. This firm, near Eagle River, became famous for its huge investments—all of them failures.

a horse. The shafts were still relatively shallow, and in some of them, and on the surface, copper was "roasted" by fire in order to break it for "barreling." The company maintained a large garden and had a powderhouse, warehouse, boardinghouse, stable, smith shop, and other outbuildings.[44] The patience and farsightedness of the Pitts-

burgh group had paid off well. At this time the board consisted of Hussey, Avery, Howe, and Pettit of Pittsburgh, and Thomas Jones and Charles Scudder of Boston.[45]

By the end of 1846 only three companies had sufficient mining to be called operating firms. Of these, only the Pittsburgh and Boston, plus the Copper Falls Company of

NORTH VIEW of COPPERFALLS WORKS.

This mining community was a few miles north of the Cliff, behind Eagle Harbor.

A view of the Cliff location, showing the rugged hills.

Eagle Harbor, had reported any copper product by the end of July. The other company, the Lake Superior now under C. C. Douglass, had a force of seventy miners but was finding little copper.[46]

The leading trade magazines of the era finally began to look on the Lake Superior mines as something more than speculation. *Hunt's Merchant's Magazine* in 1846 reported a shipment of ninety barrels of copper and silver that recently arrived at Detroit from the Cliff Mine. That particular shipment was consigned to the plant at Roxbury, Mass., while another shipment from the Cliff was sent to Buffalo. The following quotation from *Hunt's,* a nationally-known New York magazine, pretty much summed up the country's feelings about the Lake Superior country:

> Making all due allowance for the mining fever, we have no doubt that the mines in question are rich in copper and silver ores, and that they will be worked with profit and advantage to the country, as well as to the companies immediately interested.[47]

More typical of the general awareness and publicity was an article that appeared in the *New York Post* in August of 1846. A reporter inspected the copper fields and wrote that they were "more favorable than those of any copper mines in the world."[48]

1. Thomas L. McKenney and James Hall, *The Indian Tribes of North America* (Edinburgh: John Grant, 1933), I, 348-51.

2. A good collection of studies on this copper culture is in James B. Griffin (ed.), *Lake Superior Copper and the Indians: Miscellaneous Studies of Great Lakes Prehistory* (Ann Arbor: University of Michigan Museum, 1961).

3. Rueben Gold Thwaites (ed.), *Jesuit Relations and Allied Documents*, LIV, 153-59.

4. His efforts are summarized in *Dictionary of Canadian Biography* (Toronto: University of Toronto Press, 1969), II, 427-29.

5. A nasty letter from Messrs. de Beauharnois and Hocquart to the Minister of Marine, 1740, is in C 11 A, Vol. 76, p. 302, Public Archives of Canada. They suggested that what "was known of the minerals of Lake Superior do not permit any hope of success for his enterprise." A fair summary of these French expeditions appears in Louise P. Kellogg, *French Regime in Wisconsin and the Northwest* (Madison: State Historical Society, 1925), pp. 351-57.

6. Excerpts from Henry's journal and an analysis appear in *History of the Upper Peninsula of Michigan* (Chicago: Western Historical Co., 1883), pp. 131-32.

7. Porter's report appears as an appendix to Thomas L. McKenney, *Sketches of a Tour to the Lakes* (Baltimore, 1827, reprinted by Ross & Haines of Minneapolis, 1959), pp. 477-78.

8. Schoolcraft to Crawford, April 13, 1840, Records of the Michigan Indian Superintendency, Letters Sent by Superintendents at Mackinac, National Archives Microfilm Reel No. 140, copy in Michigan State Archives, Lansing.

9. J. Leander Bishop, *A History of American Manufacturers from 1608 to 1860* (Philadelphia: Edward Young & Co., 1868), II, 126, 155, 190, 403.

10. Victor S. Clark, *History of Manufacturers in the United States: Volume I, 1607-1860* (New York: Peter Smith, 1949), I, 525-26.

11. F. E. Richter, "The Copper Mining Industry in the United States," *Quarterly Journal of Economics*, XLIV (1926-1927), 238.

12. Stuart to Crawford, October 24, 1842, Letters Sent by the Superintendents at Mackinac, Reel No. 141, pp. 17-18 (outlining treaty provisions.)

13. Stuart to Cunningham, May 4, 1843; Stuart to Ord, June 6, 1843, in Letters Sent from Superintendents at Mackinac, Reel No. 141, pp. 159, 196.

14. Quoted in Robert James Hybels, "Lake Superior Copper Fever, 1841-47," *Michigan History*, XXXIV (June, 1950), 113. A recent book on this topic is Lawrence T. Fadner, *Fort Wilkins 1844, and the U. S. Mineral Land Agency, 1843* (New York: Vantage Press, 1966).

15. A lively discussion of the Eldred-Paul-Cunningham incident is in Angus Murdoch, *Boom Copper* (New York: Macmillan, 1943), pp. 73-85, although a more scholarly article is in Hybels, *Michigan History*, XXXIV (1950), 109-19. For a version favoring Paul, see the *Lake Superior Miner* (Ontonagon), September 26, 1857, p. 5.

16. The Hays-Hussey letter of agreement is in the Carnegie Library, Pittsburgh. For a description of the journey see the Hays reminiscences in Ralph D. Williams, *The Honorable Peter White* (Cleveland: Penton Publ. Co., 1907), pp. 9-11. Hays died in 1901, and some fascinating but unidentified obituaries can be found in the Daniel Brockway Papers, University of Michigan Historical Collections, Ann Arbor.

17. An entire chapter in somewhat exotic language is devoted to Hays in Murdoch, *Boom Copper*, pp. 48-58. However, there is some question about the identity of "Jim" Raymond. According to an article of agreement between Hussey and Hays, dated November 13, 1843, the leases were obtained from Daniel D. Raymond, John D. Ansley, and William R. Talmadge; agreement in the Carnegie Library, Pittsburgh. Murdoch calls him "Jim," and a J. Raymond in 1846 ran a saloon-boarding house at Copper Harbor; see *Lake Superior News and Miners' Journal* (Copper Harbor), advertisement on p. 1 of July 11, 1846.

18. A historical summary of the three leases appears in the Pittsburgh & Boston annual report for 1869, published in the *Portage Lake Mining Gazette* (Houghton), June 16, 1870, p. 2.

19. Summarized in Williams, *Peter White*, p. 10. The agreement is in the few Hussey Papers in the Carnegie Library, Pittsburgh.

20. Advertisement in the *Lake Superior News and Miners' Journal* (Copper Harbor), July 11, 1846, p. 1. This was the first issue of the first newspaper in the Lake Superior country.

21. Williams, *Peter White*, p. 10.

22. Douglass to his parents, June 23, 1844, Douglass Papers, Michigan Historical Commission, Lansing.

23. Wm. H. Stevens, "Prospects of the Lake Superior Mining Region," *Mining Magazine*, II (1854), 149-53. Stevens had earlier served as mining superintendent at the Cliff.

24. Horace V. Winchell, "Historical Sketch of the Discovery of Mineral Deposits in the Lake Superior Region," *Proceedings of the Lake Superior Mining Institute*, II, (1894), 47-48. Hussey's quote is from the annual report for 1869, in *Portage Lake Mining Gazette* (Houghton), June 16, 1870.

25. "Curtis G. Hussey," *Magazine of Western History*, III (February, 1886), 334-35.

26. The letter is in Anna Brockway Gray, "Letters from the Long Ago,"

Michigan History Magazine, XX (Spring-Summer, 1936), 190-91.

27. Robert Stuart to Chas. Borup of the LaPointe (Wis.) agency, March 4, 1844, Letters Sent by the Superintendents at Mackinac, Reel No. 141, pp. 384-85.

28. Thorough documentation on the fort can be found in the Historic Site Files, Michigan Historical Commission, Lansing. The fort was entered on the National Register of Historic Places in 1970.

29. *A True Description of the Lake Superior Country* (New York: Wm. H. Graham, 1846), pp. 28-30.

30. *Ibid.*, pp. 11-12.

31. See the excellent maps and lists of permit holders in *ibid.*

32. Williams, *Peter White*, pp. 15-16. See also the Hays obituaries in the Daniel Brockway Papers, University of Michigan Historical Collections.

33. For the Hill version see *History of the Upper Peninsula of Michigan*, pp. 134-35. For Hays' "illness" see Williams, *Peter White*, p. 15. Pettit has no bad words for anyone in his article on the Copper Country in *Journal of the Franklin Institute*, Third Series, XIII (1847), 338-45.

34. These figures are taken from a summary in *Report of the President and Directors of the Pittsburgh and Boston Mining Company* (Pittsburgh: Geo. Parkin & Co., 1849).

35. For the Hays version see Williams, *Peter White*, pp. 10-11; for Brockway's comment, see Gray, *Michigan History Magazine*, XX (1936), 190.

36. See, for example, Winchell, *Proceedings of the Lake Superior Mining Institute*, II (1894), 48, and a history of the mine published in *Annual Report of the Commissioner of Mineral Statistics* (Lansing: W. S. George & Co., 1881), p. 13.

37. *Keweenaw Miner* (Mohawk), March 11, 1916, p. 9.

38. *Portage Lake Mining Gazette* (Houghton), November 2, 1882, p. 3; July 1, 1880, p. 1; July 8, 1880, p. 3.

39. Details vary, but some sound reports of this are in J. W. Foster and J. D. Whitney, *Report on the Geology and Topography of a Portion of the Lake Superior Land District Part I, Copper Lands* (Washington: House of Representatives, 1850), pp. 127-28, and *Annual Report of the Commissioner of Mineral Statistics* (Lansing: W. S. George & Co., 1881), pp. 13-15, and the *Report . . . of the Pittsburgh and Boston Mining Company* (Pittsburgh: Geo. Parkin & Co., 1849).

40. "Early Settlement of the Copper Regions of Lake Superior," *Michigan Pioneer Collections*, VII (1884), 181-93.

41. The reports of the agent and directors appeared in the *Lake Superior News and Miners' Journal* (Copper Harbor), October 3, 1846, p. 2.

42. Summary taken from the 1849 *Report of the Pittsburgh and Boston Mining Company*.

43. This is quoted in *History of the Upper Peninsula of Michigan*, p. 134; see also J. R. Van Pelt, *Boston and Keweenaw: An Etching in Copper* (Houghton: Michigan College of Mining and Technology, 1957), p. 6.

44. Reports of the directors, agent, and smelter operator appeared in *Lake Superior News and Mining Journal* (Sault Ste. Marie), June 26, 1847, pp. 1, 3.

45. List of officers from *Lake Superior News and Miners' Journal* (Copper Harbor), August 8, 1846, p. 3.

46. Mineral agents figures are reprinted in Fadner, *Fort Wilkins and the Mineral Land Agency*, p. 105; for the Lake Superior Company see Forster, *Michigan Pioneer Collections*, VII (1884), 188.

47. *Hunt's Merchant's Magazine*, XV (1846), 105, in an article entitled "The Michigan Copper Output in 1846."

48. Article reprinted in *Niles' National Register*, September 5, 1846.

Chapter 2:

The Bonanza Years

WHAT MANNER OF LAND WAS THE KEWEENAW that it contained these brilliant chunks of pure copper? For two hundred years explorers had found pieces of this pure metal around Lake Superior, but they usually attributed it to some vague natural freak, and later generations blamed it on "glacial action." Yet, the massive chunks found at the Cliff forced a geological reappraisal, and it took decades for most of the world to realize that on the Keweenaw Peninsula miners went down in the shaft and pure copper came up.

The Keweenaw Peninsula juts some seventy miles northeast into Lake Superior, and down the peninsula runs a thin band of land averaging three to five miles in width, about 600 feet above lake level: this is the famed Michigan copper range. It is no wonder that hundreds of mining companies collapsed without finding copper, for a few feet away from the copper range an ounce of copper could seldom be found. One scientist, Dr. J. R. Van Pelt of the Michigan College of Mining and Technology, described the area as consisting of several hundred Precambrian lava flows and beds of sandstone and conglomerate, "laid one upon another like a great deck of cards miles in length, and then turned steeply on edge." The stresses that accompanied this upheaval caused the rock to break here and there in cross fissures, but the conglomerates (pudding-like, often cemented together with pure copper) and amygdaloids (pure copper in almond-shaped rock cavities) contained small particles of copper.[1]

Another way of phrasing this complicated geology is that the peninsula contains a long, broad belt of greenstone, and the great mines of the Keweenaw are directly to the south (to the right) of the greenstone belt. The Cliff, for example, is exactly at the junction of the greenstone and the main copper belt.[2] T. A. Rickard, Cornish-American mining expert, summarized some of the geological studies and also concluded that the first successful mines were those that were in the "transverse fissures crossing the Keweenaw series at the northern end of the peninsula."[3]

Angus Murdoch in *Boom Copper* gives an effective, col-

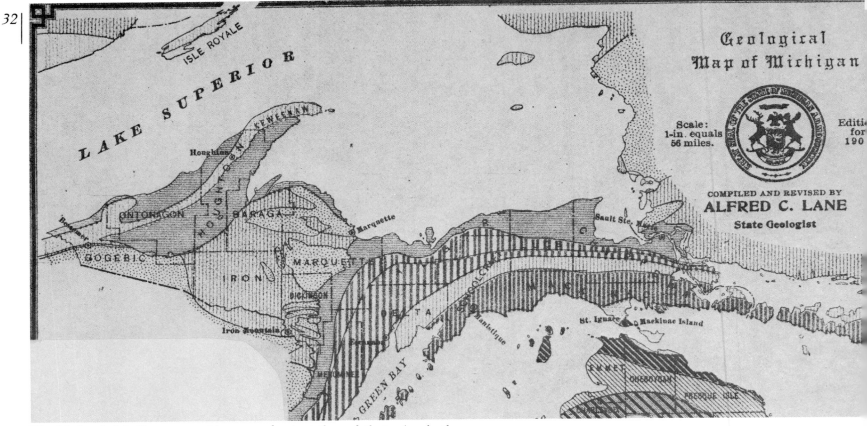

The thin band of the Keweenaw copper range shoots up through the peninsula, then goes beneath Lake Superior. Isle Royale is in the same geological formation.

orful picture of a billion-year-old copper range, vomiting its white-hot volcanic materials, each time leading to another surface layer. The copper filled the openings in the porous rock:

> After filling the mineral range to the brim, Nature found she had considerable pure, native copper left over. This extra metal then literally overflowed the range and poured into the fissures and crevices of the surrounding rock.[4]

This was how the mass copper of the Cliff, Central, Minesota, and other famous early mines was formed. Later discoveries and improved technology would lead to the ex-

ploitation of the conglomerate and amygdaloid fields to the south in Houghton County. Yet, from 1845 to 1870 the glory, the copper, and the profits went to the owners of "mass" properties, and of these the Cliff owned by the Pittsburgh group was king.

In the opening chapter the year 1847 was mentioned as one in which the Cliff, infused with Avery's money and confidence, was a hustling mine, doing very well in getting out mass copper. Horace Greeley left his editorial duties with the *New York Tribune* in the summer of 1847 and visited more than ten mining companies on the Keweenaw—he was financially interested in the Delaware and a few other properties. Greeley was no mining expert, as he admitted, but his comments on these early operations are perceptive.

Greeley described the 800-foot Cliff, its summit covered with birch and poplar, with a small stream at the base. Approaching the mine, the visitor saw "great piles of shining Native Metal," and chunks of pure copper were "profusely scattered around." Yet, what staggered Greeley were the giant copper boulders he saw in the adit.

> *They* cannot be blasted—a hundred pounds of powder would hardly throw a shillings worth of Copper; but the rock may be blasted away from them on every side, when they are ready to be cut into such pieces as may be elevated and taken out of the mine.[5]

The journalist ran out of adjectives as he praised the value of its stock, the "boundless wealth of Nature," and the "giant masses of pure Copper." Some of the masses were eight feet long, five feet wide, and two feet thick, mixed with rich native silver. Greeley said it all when he praised the Cliff as having "no rival in this region nor in the world." In late June of the year Greeley climbed his last precipice and "killed my last Keweenaw mosquito" and headed back for New York, happy to have seen the Cliff, "a manifestation of the boundless wealth of Nature."[6]

The high praise from the energetic Greeley was matched by copper production during that summer. Weekly production for July and August averaged 45,000 pounds.[7] By the time the shipping season was over, the amount sent from the docks at Eagle River was more than impressive. The Cliff shipped 1,500,000 pounds, whereas its neighbor, the Lake Superior Company, shipped only 34,441 pounds. More typical of amount of copper shipped was the Lac La Belle Company near Copper Harbor, which shipped 1,329 pounds.[8]

A correspondent for the Sault Ste. Marie newspaper toured the Cliff with Captain Edward Jennings as guide in late October of 1847 and said the mine was "at the head of all others." It was impossible to describe one copper mass, but "there is enough [in the mass] to employ one hundred

Horace Greeley.

men at least five years in taking it out." The work force was 130 at that time, but the correspondent felt that they would employ at least 200 during the winter to sink two additional shafts. A stamping facility was operating to crush the rock from the copper, but the iron used to make the machinery was not of good quality.[9]

When the spring of 1848 arrived the predictions of the previous year were realized. In May a crew of 130 men was at work, half of whom were miners. The monthly production was 400,000 pounds, and it was said that the mine staggered the belief of any one "other than a thorough-going Yankee, who has stubbornly refused for a life-time to believe in the word, *impossibility!*"[10]

The propeller "Goliath" left the Eagle River dock with a shipment in June that was typical of the rich mining that year. The vessel carried 261 tons of copper, in barrels and mass, valued at $75,000. The metal was going to the Baltimore and Cuba Smelting Works. Some of the masses weighed 3,000 pounds, "without a particle of rock attached."[11]

The problem at the Cliff was not lack of copper but how to disgorge these huge chunks from the bowels of the earth. One-third of all work and money at the mine was spent in blasting around these masses and then cutting them with three-man teams; two men alternating with sledges, while a third man held a chisel. For the smaller pieces, and those mixed with rock, a stamping mill with seven iron heads (crushers) had been installed. Each head stamped one ton a day, with a yield of 80 per cent copper.[12]

One rich account of operations at this time was penned by the Rev. John H. Pitezel, a Methodist missionary to the L'Anse Indians who was also trying to minister to the needs of the miners around Eagle River. In the summer of 1848 Captain Jennings gave Pitezel a tour of the mine and village, and the missionary would only say that the buildings "are tolerably comfortable, but not built with regard to convenience, or external neatness." A staff of 140 was at work, 80 underground. Pitezel spoke kindly of the robust, hardy miners, climbing from the mine covered with mud and dirt, drenched from head to foot, with a tin lamp or candle in a lump of wet clay attached to their hats.

Jennings showed Pitezel the office, stamps, and whim, and then the reverend was outfitted in miner's clothing; they were ready for the trip underground. They descended by ladders, nearly straight down. The guide's philosophy was: "Hold fast with your hands—never mind your feet." At the ten-fathom level they were in drift No. 2, a north-south vein. While looking around at this point Pitezel saw a copper mass of 30-50 tons which had recently been loosened by blasting. The party then went down another 60 feet to drift No. 3, where "you have evidences of an inconceivably rich mine." Soon they came to a winze, which was a tunnel from one drift to another so that air could circulate. The group then went down another 60 feet to drift No. 4, where they crawled on hands and knees over deads (broken rock) and came to a large mass of copper, about which the captain was "much elated."

Pietzel concluded his narrative by warning prospective mine visitors to go on Monday morning (when work began) or Saturday afternoon (when work ended), because at these times the mine was free from smoke. Yet, if one visited during busy times, he would also profit. Some men would be drilling, others hammering, some wheeling, others blasting. "A dismal gloom seems to pervade the whole region," but Pitezel saw the hand of God in all of the brilliant red metal.[13]

It was also in 1848 that the company corporate structure was brought up-to-date. Back in 1844 the Pittsburgh and Boston group had acted as a partnership, and on May 20, 1845, the group was organized as a joint-stock company.[14] Then, during the late 1840s, mining companies in Michigan were organized as corporations. It was permissible to organize under either Michigan law or laws of other states, though most chose Michigan.[15] The state legislature on March 18, 1848, approved "An Act to incorporate the Pittsburgh and Boston Mining Company of Pittsburgh." The company had a capital of $150,000 divided into six thousand shares. Avery, Hussey, Howe, and Thomas Bakewell

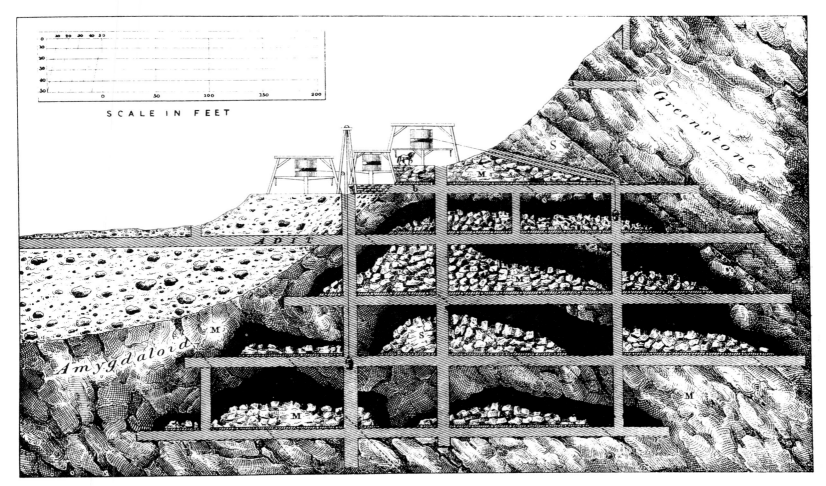

SCALE IN FEET

Geologists Foster and Whitney based this drawing on their 1849 visit to the Cliff.

were the Pittsburgh board directors; also on the board were Charles Scudder of Boston and George C. Bates of Detroit. The incorporation act provided for the company to pay an annual tax of one per cent on the amount of capital paid in and the same per cent on all sums of money borrowed by the company. The act also gave the company broad development powers, such as the authority to acquire lands and build railroads from the mines to nearby ports.[16]

In April of 1848 the stockholders paid an installment; from that time until the mine closed in 1870, the company did not need to call on the stockholders for more money. In simple language, by 1848 the stockholders had paid in $110,000; on this investment, by 1870 $2,327,660 would be returned, a phenomenal dividend history, and reason enough to call the mine the "Mighty Cliff."[17]

The boom nature of 1848 was further highlighted by the comments of Charles T. Jackson, U. S. Surveyor and prominent Boston scientist who visited the mine in August of that year. He saw miners cutting a huge 83-ton mass; one of the sections measured 4 feet by 3 feet by 1 foot. This turned out to be routine work for the Cliff crew.[18]

In January of 1849 the Pittsburgh and Boston Mining Company filed a report with the State of Michigan that was astounding. Although the company had spent money on mining, freight, stamping, smelting, taxes, and so forth, they still listed a "surplus" of $111,105.[19] The copper fields *did* have enough copper to take care of interested investors. What to do with the surplus?

The directors published a report in that month, boasting that they had overcome all obstacles and discouragements. The $111,105 was the *minimum*; in other words, the output of the Cliff was enlarging daily, and what the *permanent* character of the lode was had yet to be fully established.

Such confidence meant that the surplus was not needed, so the directors declared a dividend, the first from any mine on Lake Superior, and reportedly the first dividend from any copper mine in North America. A dividend of $10 per share was declared, payable to stockholders on May 21,

Underground work was tough, but simple. This miner has the essentials: hammer, chisel and explosives.

An example of timbering near a mine entrance, as drawn by geologists Foster and Whitney.

1849; this amounted to $60,000 for the 6000 company shares. At the same meeting the directors announced that they had abandoned the Copper Harbor lease and the lease to the west of the Cliff. They had so concentrated their efforts at the Cliff location that they took advantage of the new United States permit policy to buy the lands from the federal government: $2.50 per acre, for 4,350 acres.[20]

Towards the end of 1849 Captain Jennings played tour guide again, this time to S. V. R. Trowbridge, an agent for the United States Mineral Lands Office, now quartered at Sault Ste. Marie. After donning miner's garb, Trowbridge and Jennings descended by ladders 265 feet to the lowest level. Small rail tracks were in some of the drifts, to move the copper to a major shaft, where it would be placed in a kibble (iron bucket) and raised by whims.

Everywhere they encountered the three-man hammer-chisel teams. The chisels were about two feet long, made of the finest steel, and around two inches wide. From time to time Jennings would point to a copper mass of 123 feet, another 100 feet, and so forth. Trowbridge later wrote that the Cliff "stands now at the head of all the copper mines in the world for producing pure metal."[21]

It is not our aim to show monthly production figures for twenty years, nor to dwell at length on the size and shape of the copper masses. Yet, the mining methods devised at the Cliff were to become the standards in the mining world for some years, and these methods and tools did not drastically change during the Cliff's heyday, 1846 to 1870. Two excellent federal reports published in 1850 described these new mining techniques.

Charles T. Jackson revisited the mine at this time, guided by that "energetic Cornish miner" Captain Edward Jennings. Jackson, too, described the three-man cutting teams, but he also gave one of the earliest clear descriptions of the stamping process. A large iron stamp (crusher) broke the copper and rock into pieces weighing a few pounds each. These were then passed under other stamp-heads; while the pieces were being stamped, water pushed off some lumps

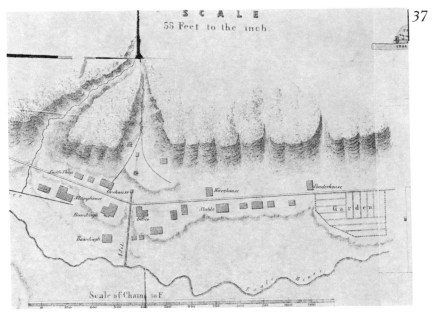

By 1849 the surface workings at the Cliff were already impressive.

This early sketch of the Cliff is invaluable for its portrayal of the various surface activities.

of copper. The remainder went through a jigging process, which agitated the pulverized bits until the copper and silver, being heavier, fell to the bottom of the watered mixture. The copper and silver were then separated, barreled, and shipped.[22]

The report of U. S. Surveyors J. W. Foster and J. D. Whitney was also published in 1850, and they discussed other aspects of the mining operations that were to remain constant over the years. Unlike Germany and Cornwall, where oak and pine were used for timbering, the Cliff used tamarack for horizontal and vertical timbering. However, Lake Superior mines in general used little timbering, except near the surface and near openings, for the shaft walls in that country were of firm rock.

By this time, too, the horse whims were being replaced by steam machinery at the Cliff and nearby mines. These whims not only lifted the copper to the surface, but they were also the only means of getting water out of the mine. Whitney had high praise for Captain Jennings, saying only in criticism that the work force should be expanded. The company was in such a hurry to cut up the masses that they neglected to make preparations for the next month's work: "The openings in the mine should be in advance of the stope work."[23]

The next few years were great for the Cliff. In 1850 the mine produced 1,028 tons of copper; the nearest competitor was the Minesota Mine on the Ontonagon Range some fifty miles to the south, which produced 257 tons.[24] In April of 1850 a further dividend was declared, at $7 a share.[25] The success, obviously, was not temporary.

Mass copper was hard to handle, and from time to time the awkwardness and weight of the mass caused problems. In May of 1851 the propeller "Manhattan" was taking on a two-ton mass from a scow at Eagle River (it was too shallow then for a dock) when the mass fell through, sinking the scow and taking down around 12,000 pounds of copper.[26]

Major improvements were being made at the Cliff, now that the parent company had surplus funds. Nicholas Vivian, a Cornish engineer headquartered in Pittsburgh, designed a forty-five-ton engine for the Cliff in 1851, "one of the best mining engines ever manufactured in this country."[27] Some mine buildings and houses were also built in that year, and a huge, five-story engine house for the stamp-heads was completed. Vivian's engine was being installed, giving sufficient power to drive thirty-six stamp-heads.[28] By spring of 1852 the entire steam engine complex was working "most beautifully." The engine was powerful enough to handle all stamping, pumping, washing tables, and so forth.[29] The work force numbered 220, of whom 90 were miners.[30]

On the evening of October 10, 1852, a fire totally destroyed the new engine house and an adjoining building, the disaster costing around $10,000. Arson was suspected, as a "villain" who had ill feeling toward the company was seen near the scene before the fire. In any case, the engines were not harmed, and a new engine house was begun at once.[31] The real problem at this time was lack of proper transportation. Three hundred tons of copper were at Eagle River awaiting shipment, but the crude rail portage around the rapids at Sault Ste. Marie slowed the whole process.[32]

Robert E. Clarke, a journalist for *Harper's New Monthly*, visited Lake Superior in the summer of 1852, and he later wrote and drew one of the most valuable early mining accounts of North America. Clarke, too, was greeted heartily

Although most of Vivian's work was for Lake Superior mines, his main office was in Pittsburgh.

by Captain Jennings and was given the grand tour. The following illustrations are from the two articles that Clarke wrote for *Harper's* about the mine, for one "has not seen mining in its best phase till he visits the Cliff."[33]

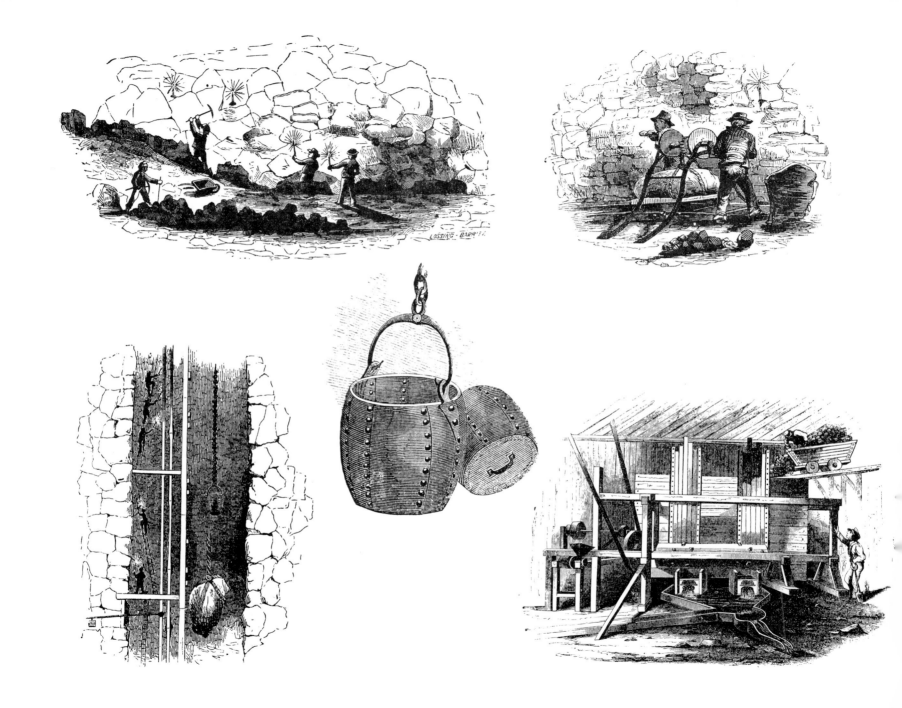

Heavy blocks of cast-iron, around 400 pounds each, propelled by an engine, were rapidly elevated and dropped on the copper rock. Then, as the crushed material moved through water at the bottom, the heaviest portion (almost pure copper) sank to the bottom, and the other, a combination of rock and copper, was pushed onward. This residue was collected and placed on "floors."

The Floors.

The "floors" were piled with "poor-stuff," where further sorting of the copper from the rock took place.

The material from the floors went to a jigger, a low brass tub with a finely perforated bottom. The workman—usually a boy—agitated the jigger; the copper pieces fell underneath the jigger. The boy then scraped the top of the jigger and threw the material into first and second bundles.

The water pushed the material over grates, which further separated the copper from rock. The monthly yield from this "poor-stuff" was eighty barrels.

First buddle

Second buddle

Cutting copper with hammer and chisel was not easy work; nor were blasting, loading, stamping, and the many other mining jobs. The Cliff wage system was adopted from that of the copper and tin mines of Cornwall, largely because of Captain Jennings and other Cornish supervisory personnel. Because this wage system—the Cornish contract—became the Lake Superior standard for decades, it deserves some explanation here.

The annual report for the Pittsburgh and Boston Company published in January of 1849 claimed that most labor at the mine was done by contracts, "which are let to the best bidders, at the commencement of every month." Surveyor Charles T. Jackson reported at this time that in the contract or piece-work system the miner received $10 per square foot of cut copper surface, measuring on one side of the cut, for dividing the copper masses.[34] This gives a good indication of how long it took the miners to cut these chunks.

The basic system for such underground work meant that approximately every sixth man contracted (after bargaining) with the mine captain as to the price per unit of measure for each job. After an agreement was reached, the contractor picked men to help him, and the work was done. As the contract was completed, the company clerk kept books which reported the production of the contractor and his crew.[35]

Probably the best, most objective summary of the contract system was given by Clarke, the *Harper's* correspondent. He pointed out that the surface men were paid flat wages of $26 a month, and for the miners:

> Stoping is paid for by the cubic fathom, in obtaining which the product of the length and breadth, the *thickness* being omitted, is divided by 36. The rate varies, from $18 to $35, according as the rock is highly compact, or of slight cohesion. Drifting—the usual size of the drift being six feet by four—is paid for at the rate of $5 the foot horizontal. For sinking a shaft, whose usual size is 10 feet by 14, the compensation is from $10 to $15 the foot vertical. For cutting copper by hammer and chisel, the workmen receive from $1.34 to $1.50 *per diem.*

The miner also had to furnish his own candles, fuse, and powder. He was forced to buy the equipment from the Pittsburgh & Boston supply store or from merchants in Eagle River at equally high prices.[36]

This contract system was fine for Cornishmen who were professional miners, but the new immigration wave after the 1870s brought thousands of Italians, Finns, Poles, and Croatians to the mining frontier, and they were not about to engage in the suicidal practice of working hard to get a day's pay. For the new miners, it would be challenge enough to stay alive. Until this immigration wave, though, the Cornish contract system prevailed.

Another example of the worth of a man's labor appeared in a summary in the *Lake Superior Journal* of September 2, 1854. The usual monthly wage for surface men was $26, teamsters $30, and $35 for "extra good hands." With these wages the laborers paid the company $10 a month for board.

During the 1850s production soared, and dividends increased. In September of 1854 a dividend of $8 per share

was declared; this made a total of $77 per share in dividends since 1849 (which came to a total of $462,000, not bad for an investment of $110,000).[37] In late summer another huge mass, at least 500 tons, was found. Some 200 tons were taken from the mass before miners noticed an even richer mass nearby. A Lansing newspaper account suggested calmly that "the effect of this upon the stock cannot but act favorably."[38] On the Boston Exchange the few available Pittsburgh & Boston Company shares were selling for $300 each.

In late 1856 the *Mining Magazine* published a summary of recent Cliff activities and concluded that more mass was being found each year. After listing the expenditures and receipts, the magazine added this note:

> Since the above Balance Sheet was made, Dividends have been declared of $10 per share, February, 1856, and $20 per share in August, making a total of $180,000.[39]

Great riches were also being spewed forth on the Ontonagon Range to the south, and by 1858 production figures showed that the Keweenaw district was no longer alone in profitable copper output. In that year on Keweenaw Point the number of mine engines operating was twenty-six (six at the Cliff), while there were sixteen engines at work on the Ontonagon Range.[40] Even more indicative of the shift are figures for copper tonnage passing through the newly opened St. Mary's Falls Ship Canal in 1857. The Cliff shipped 973 tons, but she was behind her Ontonagon Range rival, the Minesota, which shipped 1,676 tons.[41] However, this is a bit misleading, for the Cliff still had many tons of barrel work and mass at Eagle River awaiting shipment.

Throughout the 1850s about 70 per cent of the output of the Cliff was in masses, the remainder being barrel work and stamp work. During this era there was no mine in the world to compare with its richness. The Minesota approached it in production but could not equal it. The company was still so confident that in 1858 they increased the number of shares to 20,000 and organized the North Cliff Mining Company on adjacent land, ceding the new firm

Ontonagon in 1855. The four-story building is the Bigelow House.

The nearby North American Mine was absorbed into the Pittsburgh firm's operations.

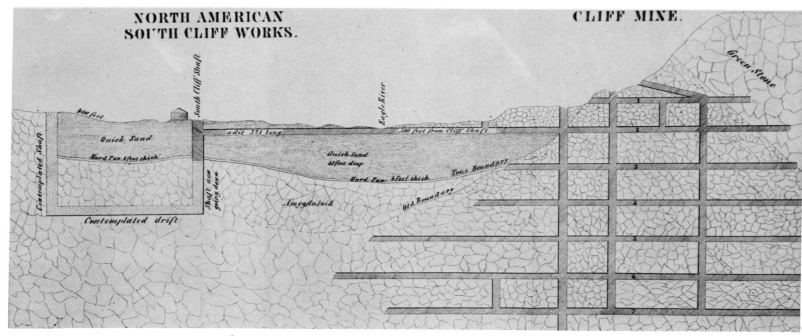

The plan for the North American works was drawn by Marquis Kelsey, Cliff supervisor.

1,000 acres and $50,000 operating cash. Silver was usually found with the copper of the Lake Superior fields, but there is no way of telling how much of the white metal was taken by the miners without, of course, reporting the finds. The Commissioner of Mineral Statistics later wrote that "but a portion of the silver actually found finds its way into the coffers of the company; not infrequently the miners regard such 'finds' as their peculiar prize, and so appropriate it to themselves."[42]

The next few years were the first in which the company optimism was challenged. Production fell from 1,180 tons in 1857 to 707 tons in 1859. The bottom level (No. 9) had been rich in amygdaloid, but that was fairly well exhausted. Also, the shaft depth was now nearing 1,000 feet, and copper masses were not appearing so regularly. In spite of these negative signs, the company expanded in 1860 by buying out the North American Mining Company,

a 2,300-acre firm, for $100,000. This company, adjacent to the Cliff, had been working with little success since 1852, and the Pittsburgh and Boston Company was never able to make the new acquisition a profitable concern.[43]

In the last year of the decade—1859—the depth of the mine "seriously embarrassed" the operations, and the "unproductive character of the eighty fathoms level" caused declining production, so much so that for the first time since 1849 a dividend was not declared. There were other signs of weariness. The Cornish battery of thirty-six stamp heads and the stamping engines had to be overhauled, and to do this the Cliff had to shut down stamping for a month.[44]

After more than a decade of being the richest copper mine in the world, the Cliff was beginning to tire. New mining methods, new personnel, new equipment, or higher prices for copper would be needed before the Cliff would be restored to its former degree of productivity.[45]

1. Van Pelt, *Boston and Keweenaw*, p. 7.

2. Michigan, *Annual Report, Commissioner of Mineral Statistics, 1880*, pp. 11-12.

3. T. A. Rickard, *The Copper Mines of Lake Superior* (New York: Engineering & Mining Journal, 1905), p. 25. See also an article on the same subject by Rickard in the *Native Copper Times* (Lake Linden, Mich.), November 1, 1904.

4. Murdoch, *Boom Copper*, p. 40. These few paragraphs on the origin of the copper fields might appear vague, but such is the state of geology. For example, the most recent publication states that "there has been considerable argument concerning the mode of origin of the native copper deposits;" John A. Dorr, Jr., and Donald F. Eschman, *Geology of Michigan* (Ann Arbor: University of Michigan Press, 1970), p. 74.

5. *New-York Weekly Tribune*, July 17, 1847, a series of letters from Keweenaw.

6. *Ibid.* His enthusiasm for all mining faded over the years. In his autobiography he still mentioned good words for the Cliff, but chances anywhere of a good strike are "as one to a million. As a rule, there are many easier ways of gaining gold than digging it from the earth; yet let all dig who will;" *Recollections of a Busy Life* (New York: J. B. Ford & Co., 1868), p. 246.

7. *Lake Superior News and Mining Journal* (Sault Ste. Marie, Mich.), October 2, 1847.

8. *Ibid.*, October 20, 1847.

9. *Ibid.*, November 8, 1847.

10. *Ibid.*, May 20, 1848.

11. *Ibid.*, June 23, 1848.

12. *Ibid.*, see also issue of July 28, 1848.

13. John H. Pitezel, *Lights and Shades of Missionary Life* (Cincinnati: Western Book Concern, 1859), pp. 165-74.

14. This is from a history of the company published in the annual report for 1869, in the *Portage Lake Mining Gazette* (Houghton, Mich.), June 16, 1870.

15. William B. Gates, Jr., *Michigan Copper and Boston Dollars* (Cambridge: Harvard University Press, 1951), p. 31.

16. Michigan, *Acts of the Legislature* (1848), No. 85. Bates was a flamboyant attorney very active in Whig politics at this time. His later interests in mining took him to the Rocky Mountains in the 1880's. He died in Denver in 1886; obituary in *Michigan Pioneer Collections*, IX (1886), 87.

17. *Portage Lake Mining Gazette*, April 13, 1876.

18. Charles T. Jackson's Land Office Report is in U.S. Congress, House, *Message From the President of the United States*, 31st Cong., 1st Sess., Ex. Doc. No. 5, Part III, 1849.

19. Filed in Corporation Annual Reports, 61-11-A, Lot 3, Box 1, State Archives, Michigan Historical Commission, Lansing.

20. *Report of the President and Directors of the Pittsburgh and Boston Mining Company* (Pittsburgh: George Parkin & Co., 1849); see also, Michigan, *Annual Report, Commissioner of Mineral Statistics, 1880*, p. 14.

21. The Trowbridge report to the Michigan Secretary of State is in *Joint Documents of the Legislature* (1850), pp. 53-59.

22. Jackson's Land Office Report, pp. 434-35.

23. Foster and Whitney, *Copper Lands*, pp. 127-29.

24. Seventh Census of the United States (1850): Industry, p. 278, original in the Michigan State Archives.

25. *Lake Superior Journal* (Sault Ste. Marie), May 1, 1850.

26. *Ibid.*, May 28, 1851.

27. *Ibid.*

28. *Ibid.*, October 29, 1851.

29. *Ibid.*, June 5, 1852.

30. *Ibid.* (Detroit), March 1, 1852. The title of this newspaper changed slightly four times; it began publishing in Copper Harbor in 1846, moved to the Sault the following years, and for the next few years was published at the Sault during the shipping season and in Detroit in the winter.

31. *Ibid.* (Sault), October 20, November 10, 1852.

32. *Ibid.*, November 10, 1852.

33. *Harper's New Monthly Magazine*, VI (March, 1853), 438-48, and VI (April, 1853), 577-88.

34. Jackson's Land Office Report, p. 435.

35. *Mining Magazine*, I (1853), 294.

36. Clarke, *Harper's New Monthly Magazine*, VI (April, 1853), 581.

37. *Report of the President and Directors of the Pittsburgh and Boston Mining Company* (Pittsburgh: W. S. Haven, 1854), p. 12.

38. *Lansing State Republican*, August 28, 1855.

39. *Mining Magazine*, VII (1856), 520.

40. *Detroit Daily Free Press*, February 21, 1857.

41. Report in the Papers of the Executive Office, Box 262, folio 22, Michigan State Archives.

42. Michigan, *Annual Report, Commissioner of Mineral Statistics, 1880*, pp. 16-17. See p. 21 for silver quotation.

43. *Ibid.*, pp. 16-18. See also in the appendix of the 1880 report a list of copper production for all Lake Superior mines, 1855-1880.

44. Summarized in the *Report of the President and Directors of the Pittsburgh and Boston Mining Company* (Pittsburgh: W. S. Haven, 1860).

45. *Ibid.*

Chapter 3:

War Years and Bad Years: The 1860's

GOOD NEWS was the word at the beginning of the decade, according to a report signed by President C. G. Hussey in November of 1860. Apparently in 1858 and 1859 some bad moves had been made by the engineering staff at the Cliff, and at the eighty-fathom level the crews lost the main lode of mass copper. However, early in 1860 the main lode was found again. The results were noteworthy: in 1859 only 968,000 pounds of mass were mined, but this increased to 1,200,000 pounds in 1860. Hussey also detailed the results of surveys and studies which were leading to increased production of amygdaloid copper. This amygdaloid, a product worked over in the stamping process, amounted to 800,000 pounds in 1860, almost half of the firm's total copper production.[1]

The mine agent at this time was John Slawson, and his report gives us a clear picture of the mine community at the beginning of the decade. The population of the village—called Clifton—was 1,443, and of these, 215 were miners and 244 were management and surface hands (teamsters, farm hands, blacksmiths, etc.). Of the surface crew, about fifty were in the stamping division, and many of these were boys in their early teens. In addition to making normal repairs of machinery, the staff also built a 147' x 36' mineral house, a new engine house, some boarding houses, and a "neat and commodious office for the physicians at the mine."[2]

When the Civil War began in 1861 the Cliff was in the midst of sound recovery, but the war caused some unusual situations in copper production, and historians still do not agree on all of the causes and results. For example, the price of copper rose during the war, but production in most mines declined. Why this output decreased can be answered by examining the overall impact of the war on copper mining in general, and on the Cliff Mine in particular.

Up to the time of the war, most of the nation's copper was used for sheathing of wooden ships, coins, pots and pans, telegraph wires, and various brass products. The war created a demand for such products as brass buttons, copper canteens, bronze cannons, and naval equipment. Earli-

Mass copper, a product made famous by the Lake Superior mines.

er uses for copper were expanded; for example, many more copper telegraph wires were needed for the battle areas.[3]

A glance at some production figures for the war years shows the two leading mines for each of the three mining ranges in the Copper Country: the Keweenaw, Ontonagon, and Portage Lake. Of the three ranges, the Portage Lake

was the youngest (mid-1850s), and unlike the other two ranges, it mined amygdaloid rather than mass copper.

By the end of the Civil War the Portage Lake district was the leading copper producer, as the depth of the mass mines to the north and south made profits more difficult to earn, and the deeper the mass mines went, the thinner the mass became. During the war years most companies did fairly well, though, as the Cliff paid almost $1,000,000 in dividends. The Minesota and National also paid handsome dividends, and by the middle of the war the Portage Lake mines were also paying excellent dividends.[5]

The Cliff struggled to maintain her production reputation in 1863. A report for March of that year listed the Cliff product at 150 tons, while the Minesota had 111 and the Quincy 74. A few months later, in May, the Cliff was still the leading mine in the Copper Country "patriotic production" race, although still being pushed by the Minesota and Quincy.[6]

Rising prices for copper and increased production at the Cliff led to encouraging words from C. G. Hussey in the directors' report published in May of 1863. He wrote of the fine staff, increased tonnage, good prices, and sound future. Yet, much of Hussey's report was aimed at "malicious" propaganda directed at the firm from the *Boston Journal*.

The stockholders had a meeting in Boston early in 1863, and some expressed displeasure at the way the company was so rapidly selling its supply of copper. After all, they reasoned, in a period of rising prices, why not stockpile it for awhile? In a series of articles in February the *Journal* took the side of the dissident stockholders. Hussey replied that to withhold the copper from the market was speculation, which the company discouraged. Furthermore, who could tell what the market would be next week? Confederate and Union victories were hard to predict, yet each major victory affected the market. Hussey claimed that their experiences in New York and Pittsburgh, where most of the copper was sold, led the company to believe that it was "much safer for the producer to meet the consumer with

PRODUCTION FIGURES FOR THE WAR YEARS[4]
(tons)

	1861	1863	1865
KEWEENAW			
Cliff	964	1,050	747
Central	70	278	546
PORTAGE LAKE			
Quincy	1,282	1,115	923
Pewabic	924	845	865
ONTONAGON			
Minesota	1,508	838	201
National	691	280	348

Mass copper was prized, but no quick, efficient method was found to cut the copper.

The Cliff production for 1863 was 1,050 tons; 1,057 in 1864; and 747 in 1865. As was mentioned earlier, some historians have wondered why, in the face of rising prices for copper, did the production of the Michigan mines decline. Most of the answer lies in a terrific labor shortage at this time, largely due to hundreds of men enlisting in the Union Army. For example, a huge parade was held in Eagle Harbor in late 1862, and from there 1,500 men marched to Eagle River and the Cliff Mine on a recruiting mission. Dozens of miners signed the Union roster.[8] During the war Keweenaw County provided more soldiers in proportion to its population than most other regions in the state, a circumstance welcomed by the recruiters, but one which horrified the profit-conscious mine owners.[9] The mining frontier, of course, was populated primarily by young, single males. For many of them, service in the army was more attractive than work at the 800-foot level; yet, other young men feared the draft, and some fled to Canada. Of the three mining districts, the Keweenaw and Ontonagon suffered most, for they relied on Cornish, Irish, and native American labor. The Portage Lake mines, particularly the Quincy, did much to encourage immigration, and almost a thousand mine laborers were obtained from Scandinavia and Canada.[10]

DRILLING IN A COPPER MINE

his article...ready for delivery...than to speculate upon chances." In conclusion, Hussey pointed out that the *Boston Journal* had criticized the company without realizing that their procedure was in no way different from that of the other major Michigan mines.[7]

A mineral exploring crew of 1863. Seated at right, is Henri F. Q. d'Aligny, French mining engineer who had an office in Copper Harbor.

A Harper's artist sketched this Indian packer who worked with a copper exploring party.

When the Cliff began using its new "Man Engine," miners on the European mainland were descending shafts in a variety of primitive ways.

Yet, there were other reasons for labor shortages, especially at the Cliff. By the summer of 1864 "men were daily leaving, and not one applying for labor, and the working force was at one time reduced to 70 miners."[11] This was indeed a startling figure for a prosperous mine that had formerly employed 250 miners. The reason for this labor shortage was the great depth of the mine, which led to all sorts of problems. By this time many of the men were working 800 and 1,000 feet underground, and after a hard day's labor they spent nearly an hour climbing the dangerous ladders to the surface. In a labor-scarce situation, the men did not have to put up with such strenuous, dangerous work, and many of them drifted south a few miles to the mines of the Portage Lake district.[12]

This labor shortage caused by the miner's reluctance to scale 1,000 feet of ladders was studied by the company in 1864, and the problem was solved by introducing a "Man Engine," the first in any mine in North America. These lifting devices had been in use in Cornwall as early as 1841.[13] J. W. Rawlins, a Cornishman who had arrived at the Cliff in 1850 and worked his way up to the position of leading mechanic-engineer, drew up the design for the Man Engine and was in charge of all phases of construction. According to Rawlins:

> The Agent ask'd me if I knew anything about the Man Engine, I told him I had never seen one, but as there was only one way to work it, I didn't think it a difficult proposition.

Rawlins designed a machine, and the plans were sent to Pittsburgh for examination. The company through the agent told Rawlins to go ahead, "for now he was certain I knew my business."[14]

The Man Engine was a technological breakthrough for the deep mines, and most mines in the Copper Country adapted its principles. The men were hoisted from the mine on a series of platforms (21" x 21") fastened to a vertical spruce connecting rod. These rods were fastened to bobs, which were moved by the king posts, which received their power from the engine. The rods were moved in such a way that

John Rawlins, inventor of the "Man Engine."

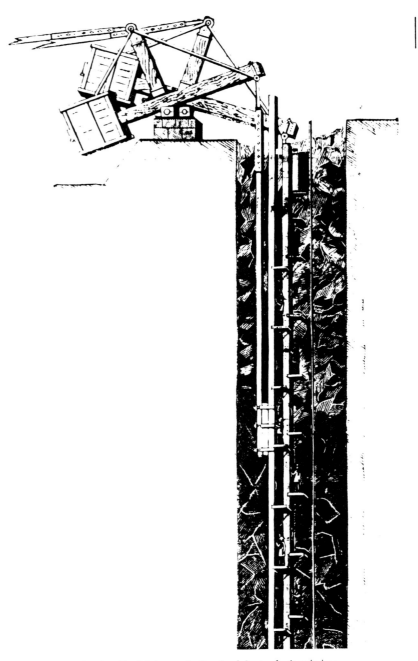

The "Man Engine," which revolutionized deep-shaft mining.

while one rod descended, the other ascended. The rods were 720' long. The Man Engine worked so well that the entire crew could be removed from the mine in thirty minutes.[15]

The Man Engine began operations on January 2, 1865, the work being pushed by Rawlins, who "kept the thing a-going until I had the machine finish'd and the men a riding."[16] The *Mining Gazette* welcomed this mechanical advance: "When its humane and beneficial effects have become more fully known and appreciated, we hope to see its precedent followed by every mine in the country working below their fifth or sixth levels."[17]

There were other mining innovations at this time that resulted in better working conditions. In 1865 the Houghton firm of P. R. Gottstein & Co. developed a new mining candle with "wicks of the right size, are not soft, and consequently do not melt away in an hour, are not scaly, and can stand rough handling without breaking into pieces."[18] Another major change was made at the Cliff in 1866 when Bessemer steel replaced the wrought iron in the stamping machinery.[19]

Mining machinery and company wishes are not enough to insure mineral production, and the Pittsburgh and Boston firm was faced with several circumstances that led to its demise. The Civil War was over, and so were the rapid price rises for copper, as well as the demand for military uses for the metal. Furthermore, foreign copper production, as well as increased production from California mines, also competed for the Michigan copper markets. For example, in the early 1850s much of the copper from the Cliff went to the Baltimore and Cuba Smelting Works. Yet, by the 1860s the Baltimore firm was using copper primarily from Chile, Cuba, and Africa. This was so because unlike iron and other metals, copper from foreign countries faced only a token tariff. As foreign producers took advantage of the situation, the Lake Superior mines began to suffer. True, this was only a temporary situation, but it was enough to seriously cripple the Cliff at that time.[20]

The year 1866 was the last good one for the Cliff, yet at

The Old Cliff Takes the Lead !

Our telegraph dispatches announce to us this morning that the gallant old Cliff Mine has declared a semi-annual dividend of THREE DOLLARS PER SHARE, payable August 6th. The "Small Stockholder" will undoubtedly feel jubilant over this very strong indication of a "shower of dividends," and entertain livelier hopes of the future. What other mine is going to follow suit ? If none, then they can but acknowledge the Cliff has been more economically managed and energetically worked than any other mine in the country, notwithstanding the continual reports that "the Cliff is looking poor." This last $60,000 makes the total amount paid in by stockholders.

By the mid-1860s this type of news was rare.

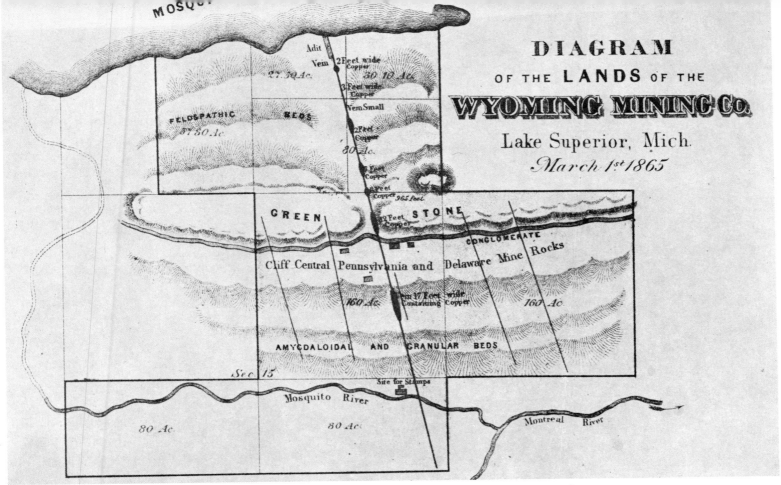

DIAGRAM
OF THE LANDS OF THE
WYOMING MINING CO.
Lake Superior, Mich.
March 1st 1865

The Wyoming was miles north of the Cliff, but Sam Hill, who made this map, tried to convince stockholders that what happened at Cliff could happen at Wyoming.

the time the management did not realize this. In late July the Cliff declared a semi-annual dividend of $3 a share, and the *Mining Gazette* declared: "The Cliff has been more economically managed and energetically worked than any other mine in the country, notwithstanding the continual reports that 'the Cliff is looking poor.' "[21] The annual report for 1866 showed that production was slightly better than the previous year. Employment was up, thanks largely to the efficient Man Engine, which "is giving perfect satisfaction." There were 181 miners and a surface crew of 140. An ominous note was present in Hussey's

report, though, for he acknowledged that no new major lodes were discovered during the year.[22]

Mining language tended towards optimistic predictions, but in the past the Cliff had usually reported only what it knew to be true. In 1867, though, the Cliff management began to grope for signs of success like any of the dozens of other local mines. In May the mine captain theorized that a tremendous mass had been found, large enough to be continuous between two levels, a distance of seventy-two feet. His proof:

But one piece of five thousand pounds has been cut off, and

when the blast was fired to throw it out, the workmen above them saw the upper end shake. To prove this, one of the captains held his hand on the top while another struck hard on the bottom with a hammer. The captain is certain he felt the jar of the blow.[23]

This was the type of language usually peddled by firms named Eldorado, Eureka, and Bonanza, and to have Pittsburgh and Boston men passing on such stories was not encouraging.

Hussey, too, fell into the hope-for-the-best syndrome, as his annual report for 1868 claimed "indications are of a much more favorable character." This is strange optimism, for the output was only sixty tons better than the previous year.[24]

The true measure of conditions was to be found in the annual production for the late 1860s, due solely to the circumstance that the mass copper was running out, the mine shafts were too deep, and although the amygdaloid copper was rich, the amygdaloid mines to the south were closer to the surface:

1866	821 (tons)
1867	560
1868	613
1869	362
1870	222[25]

Pessimism prevailed in early 1870, as the only serious work had to be stopped because the vein was only a few inches wide. At the annual meeting of the directors in Pittsburgh in May it was decided to suspend operations after June. The *Mining Gazette* reported that "THE FATE OF THE OLD MINE IS SEALED."

> Like the Minesota, the mine may be worked a few months longer by buzzard tributors, till the last particle of value is gone, and then be allowed to fill and decay. Too bad, after such splendid results, yet it is wisdom to stop work when there is no apparent chance of profit.[26]

When the patient is ill the doctor is called, so in the summer of 1869 Samuel W. Hill, the master of profanity and famous surveyor-explorer-mine manager was hired to look for new veins on the Cliff lands. According to Hussey, Hill submitted a favorable report, but Hill could only suggest further explorations. Hill based his suggestion on the belief that the Cliff lands were close to the famous Calumet conglomerate lodes to the south, which were opened in the mid-1860s.[27]

In an article entitled "CLIFF FINIS" the *Mining Gazette* mentioned that the pump was stopped in late June and the old mine was filling up with water.

> It is so customary, when a mine is stopped, for some to start a mysterious tale about the "blocks of good ground left" here and there, and insinuate that "some one will make a good thing, some day," that it would be remarkable if the same was not said of the Cliff. But take the reports of the last two or three years' operations and see how much money the one company has made. The figures of those reports show stronger than any fatherless rumor.[28]

Sam Hill did some further mineral hunting in the summer of 1870, but nothing exciting was discovered. By autumn the Cliff crew was scavenging, a tremendous comedown for this once world-famous mine. The rock piles which had accumulated in twenty years were picked over by eighty men. About thirty-six tons of mineral were obtained in this manner, enough to pay expenses. Over fifty fathoms of water were in the old mine by the end of the year. The mine was dead, merely awaiting its official death certificate.[29]

Some work on the rock piles continued in 1871, and at the annual meeting held in Pittsburgh in October the company decided to clean up and protect the mine machinery and look for a buyer.[30] In December, 1871, the Pittsburgh and Boston Mining Company sold the Cliff property to Marshall Simpson of New York and Boston for $100,000.[31] The glory and profit days for the company were over. From the time of its first dividend in 1849, the company missed dividend payments only in 1860 and 1868-70. The company paid out to stockholders $2,327,660, all on an investment of $110,000. Or, as Hussey reminded everyone, "a little over two thousand per centum on the capital paid in."[32]

MANHATTAN MINING COMPANY.

INCORPORATED UNDER THE GENERAL LAW OF THE STATE OF MICHIGAN.

No. *1351*

SHARES *650*

CAPITAL STOCK $ 500,000 Shares $25 Each.

This Certifies, that A B Hill Trustee *the Proprietor of* Six Hundred Fifty *Shares in the Capital Stock of the* **MANHATTAN MINING COMPANY,** *transferable only on the books of said Company by the holder hereof in person or by Attorney on surrender of this Certificate.*

This Certificate to be valid only when countersigned by H.W. Nelson of Boston.

Signed at New York, *this* 2 *day of* Oct 1866

Countersigned

President

Secretary

Know all Men by these Presents, That _____ the undersigned, for value received, do hereby irrevocably constitute and appoint _____ to be _____ true and lawful attorney for _____ and in _____ name and behalf to sell, assign and transfer unto _____ or any other person or persons _____ Shares in the Manhattan Mining Company. And further one or more persons under _____ to substitute with like power In Witness whereof _____ have hereunto set _____ hand and seal this _____ day of _____ 186__ Witnesses present.

This firm, immediately to the south of the Cliff, never amounted to much. In later years, it was absorbed by the Ojibway Mining Company.

1. *Report of the President and Directors, 1860.*

2. Slawson's report is in *ibid.*

3. Gates, *Michigan Copper and Boston Dollars*, pp. 7-8.

4. Michigan, *Annual Report, Commissioner of Mineral Statistics, 1880*, statistical chart in appendix.

5. Gates, *Michigan Copper and Boston Dollars*, pp. 216-20; see also Lewis Beeson and Victor F. Lemmer, *Effects of the Civil War on Mining in Michigan* (Lansing: Michigan Civil War Centennial Observance Commission, 1966).

6. *Mining Gazette* (Houghton, Mich.), March 7 and May 16, 1863.

7. A four-column directors report by Hussey appears in *Mining Gazette*, May 23, 1863.

8. *Keweenaw Miner*, March 11, 1916, summary of Civil War impact on the Cliff.

9. *Mining Gazette*, July 11, 1863.

10. *Ibid.*, May 16 and June 27, 1863. See also Gates, *Michigan Copper and Boston Dollars*, pp. 97-98.

11. The annual report for 1864 is in the *Mining Gazette*, February 4, 1865.

12. Gates, *Michigan Copper and Boston Dollars*, pp. 97-98.

13. A. K. Hamilton Jenkin, *The Cornish Miner: An Account of His Life Above and Underground from Early Times* (London: Geo. Allen & Unwin, 1927), p. 184.

14. Rawlins, "Recollections of a Long Life," in *Copper Country Tales* (Calumet: Roy Drier, Publ., 1967), p. 116.

15. *Mining Gazette*, February 4, 1865.

16. Rawlins, *Copper Country Tales*, p. 116.

17. *Mining Gazette*, February 4, 1865.

18. *Ibid.*, July 8, 1865, August 9, 1866.

19. *Ibid.*, January 26, 1866.

20. "Report of the United States Revenue Commission in respect to copper mining and manufactures," *Reports of a Commission Appointed for a Revision of the Revenue System of the United States* (Washington: Government Printing Office, 1866), pp. 294-95.

21. *Mining Gazette*, August 2, 1866.

22. Annual report for 1866 is in *Mining Gazette*, April 18, 1867.

23. *Ibid.*, May 23, 1867.

24. Annual report for 1868 is in *Mining Gazette*, April 8, 1869.

25. Michigan, *Annual Report, Commissioner of Mineral Statistics, 1880*, chart in appendix.

26. *Portage Lake Mining Gazette* (Houghton), May 26 and June 2, 1870. By the late 1860s the *Mining Gazette* added the words Portage Lake to its masthead.

27. *Ibid.*, June 16, 1870, includes Hussey's annual report for 1869, as well as Hill's exploration report.

28. *Ibid.*, June 30, 1870.

29. *Ibid.*, August 4, August 25, September 15, November 10, December 3, 1870.

30. *Ibid.*, October 12, October 26, 1871.

31. Michigan, *Annual Report, Commissioner of Mineral Statistics, 1880*, p. 19.

32. A good dividend chart for all Lake Superior mines is in Gates, *Michigan Copper and Boston Dollars*, pp. 216-17; for Hussey comments see *Portage Lake Mining Gazette*, April 13, 1876.

Chapter 4:

The National and International Scene

THE DEMAND for the native Lake Superior copper was great, but the mechanics of getting it to market, processing it, and distributing the finished product took a decade or two to work out. Another pleasant circumstance without precedent was learning how to spend the hundreds of thousands of dollars profit from the Lake Superior diggings. The Pittsburgh and Boston Mining Company became a national leader in refining and marketing, and as we shall see in this chapter, Hussey, Avery, Howe *et al* did not need much time to learn how to spend lavishly the fruits of their investments.

The St. Mary's Rapids at Sault Ste. Marie was one of the first challenges faced by the new copper and iron giants of Lake Superior. By the late 1840's both the Keweenaw and Ontonagon copper ranges were in production, as was the newly opened iron range near modern Marquette. Crude but adequate dock and pier facilities were built at Ontonagon, Eagle River, and Carp River (Marquette). From these points the copper and iron were loaded on boats which then carried the metal to the end of the lake, Sault Ste. Marie. The "Napoleon" and the "Peninsula" were two of the busiest boats engaged in this Lake Superior traffic. Once at the Sault, the boats ended their missions because of the rapids, which descended gradually twenty feet to the level of the St. Mary's River (the same level as Lake Huron).[1]

At the Sault the cargo was placed on horse-drawn railway cars, which traveled down the main street of the town to the St. Mary's River. English traveler Laurence Oliphant visited the Sault during this era and rode one of the tramcars to the dock. He was gazing in awe at the 6,000-pound copper masses, when an acquaintance offered him a cigar. He lit the cigar and then noticed some "little black suspicious-looking grains, jolting up through a crack in the lid, revealed to me the horrifying fact that we were seated upon a barrel of gunpowder."[2]

When tram-cars stopped, the copper and iron were loaded on boats bound south to industrial centers. A typical notice in the Sault paper reported that the "Goliath" with Captain Palmer left the Sault on August 7, 1848, with a

Sault Ste. Marie, before the building of the canal. The tracks ran between Lake Superior and the St. Mary's River.

load of Cliff mass copper, destined for smelters in Pittsburgh and Baltimore.[3]

The 800 inhabitants at the Sault included Frenchmen, Indians, half-breeds, and hangers-on of the mining frontier. Traveler Oliphant thus described them:

> Square-built German fraus sat astride huge rolls of bedding displaying stout legs, blue worsted stockings, and hob-nailed shoes. Sallow Yankees, with straw-hats, swallow-tailed coats, and pumps, carried their little all in their pockets; and having nothing to lose and everything to gain in the western world to which they were bound, whittled, smoked, or chewed cheerfully. Hard-featured, bronzed miners, having spent their earnings in the bowling saloons at the Sault, were returning to the bowels of the earth gloomily.[4]

European powers had long recognized the significance of the Sault, as early as 1671 when Sieur de St. Lusson took possession of the land in the name of the king of France; Fathers Jacques Marquette and Claude Dablon had established a Jesuit mission there in 1668. In the 1750's the first military post was built there, a small establishment called Fort de Repentigny (named for the founder, Louis Le Gardeur, Sieur de Repentigny). After the War of 1812 the United States government decided to build a string of frontier army posts, and the Sault was selected as a key site. General Hugh Brady and two companies of infantry arrived in 1822 and built Fort Brady. This fort, originally built to maintain peace on the frontier and regulate Indian affairs, would take on a new mission after the building of the canal at the Sault.[5]

That the Sault was the gateway to the north was known to all, but until the discovery of rich metals there was not sufficient need or interest in building a canal there. To the fur traders who had passed here for 200 years, the portage at the rapids was just one of dozens they faced.[6] In the 1830s there was agitation in Michigan to build a canal, but petty arguments between federal and state officials over control of the project doomed its reality.[7]

Yet, when a need was established, and money was available, the petty squabbles ended. The copper was piling up on Lake Superior docks, and north-bound supplies were choking the Sault. Shippers, landowners, and mine operators vigorously pushed for a navigable connection between Lakes Superior and Huron, and in 1852 Congress responded with a land grant that would make a canal possible. At once Eastern capitalists saw the money to be made by building a canal—and getting the land grant. A group headed by Erastus Fairbanks of Vermont and Erastus Corning of Albany took the initiative and received the backing of Detroit capitalists John W. Brooks and James F. Joy. Thanks to the efforts of their agent Charles T. Harvey, a bill was passed in 1853 in the Michigan legislature authorizing the Corning-Fairbanks group to build a canal at the Sault.[8]

Harvey was appointed general agent for the new St. Mary's Falls Ship Canal Company, and he arrived at the Sault and began work in June of 1853. At one time more than 1,000 men were working on the project, digging out the solid rock and putting in the sides of the locks. Some work even continued during the fiercely cold winters; Harvey was given two years to complete the job, and he performed well. Two locks, 70 feet wide, 350 feet long, and 13 feet deep were built. The first vessel to use the canal was the steamer "Illinois," Captain Jack Wilson, on June 18, 1855. A new era was opened in Great Lakes transportation,

The opening of the Soo Canal in 1855; the rails and cars along the side would soon become obsolete.

The locks that were in continued use from 1855 to 1887.

The propeller "Mineral Rock," typical of mid-century lake boats.

and the smelters of Pittsburgh, Cleveland, Detroit, Boston, and Baltimore could look forward to receiving increased shipments of native Lake Superior copper. The Pittsburgh and Boston Mining Company was so enthusiastic over the opening of the Sault Canal that they purchased early in 1856 the steamer "Iron City," with Captain Ed Turner as master. Captain George McKay served as mate during the late 1850s, and he "never worked harder in his life." All of the loading was done by hand, and everyone on board helped out.[9]

National fame came to the Cliff and a few other mines in the late 1840s, but after the California gold rush of 1848 the country's press became infatuated with gold metal at the expense of red. As a result of this shift in publicity, some Eastern money went west instead of north. The Lake Superior operators regretted being replaced in the nation's spotlight. The *Lake Superior Journal* in 1850 reported a shipment of Cliff copper weighing 170 tons, valued at $30,000, carried by the propeller "Independence":

> When our Lake Superior shores contain such boundless wealth, it seems unaccountable that more capitalists do not turn their attentions to these *placers* of more certain riches than those of California.[10]

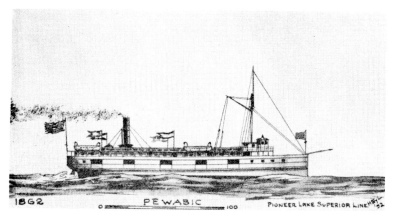

1862   PEWABIC   100   PIONEER LAKE SUPERIOR LINE

This passenger and freight vessel stopped often at Eagle River for Cliff copper shipments.

The romance of California did wear off after a few years, although the frenzied, speculative days of the northern copper fields never returned. Instead, the solid, lengthy success of mines like the Cliff gradually earned the respect of national and international newspapers and trade journals. The *Boston Journal, Pittsburgh Gazette, New York Tribune,* and *Detroit Daily Free Press* regularly reported the new successes and major shipments from the Cliff.

During the 1850s the leading mining publication was the *Mining Magazine* of New York, a monthly. Practically every issue of the magazine contained Cliff reports, notice of personnel changes, and equipment innovations. In one issue it was recommended that the village built for Cliff workers be adopted as a model for all mining communities in the nation.[11]

The *Pittsburgh Gazette* emphasized the company financial gains, but from the beginning it also carried stories that featured unusual or rich finds. In 1847 the paper announced that huge copper and silver specimens were on display at the Hussey office on Fourth Street. "The more we see and learn of the mineral capacity of the Upper Lake Country, the more amazed we are at its riches and beauty."

In the summer of 1851 the *Gazette* reported a Cliff mass of 300 tons, "and the miners have not yet reached either the end or the top of the sheet."[12]

The Detroit newspapers gave frequent coverage to the Lake Superior mines, and they often quoted at length from articles in other newspapers, especially those from the Sault, Ontonagon, Green Bay, and Cleveland. A typical tonnage report appeared in the *Detroit Daily Free Press* of April 30, 1858, mentioning that the propeller "Iron City" arrived with a load of 200 tons of Cliff copper destined for the Detroit Smelting Works. An issue of the same paper on March 8, 1855, discussed the unemployment problem on Lake Superior, largely due to a shipment of explosives that had sunk with the "Peninsula" the previous year off Eagle River. Most newspapers practiced the art of copying good stories from other sources, and the *Detroit Free Press* of January 22, 1850, carried the practice further than usual by reprinting a Cliff Mine financial report from the *Pittsburgh Post,* which had previously copied it from *Hunt's Merchants' Magazine.*

European miners and financiers were fascinated with accounts of pure copper being found, and for a few years they regarded the reports as exaggerations. The first Frenchman to visit the region in modern times was Edward Verneuil, president of the Geological Society of France, who toured the Keweenaw mines in 1846. By the mid-1850s the Paris firm of Messrs. Rothschilds & Co. were regularly receiving shipments of Lake Superior copper.[13]

French interest in Lake Superior was quickened after an inspection tour in 1854 by L.-E. Rivot, a professor in the School of Mines, Paris. He visited all three of the copper ranges and was particularly impressed with the Cliff Mine. Rivot cautioned against hasty speculation without thorough testing. Of all the mines he visited he thought that the Cliff "was in a more favorable position than any other mine on Keweenaw Point." Rivot's praise was the seal of approval, for his articles on the subject appeared in Europe's foremost trade journal, *Annales des Mines.*[14]

Because of the Cornish mining tradition, England was

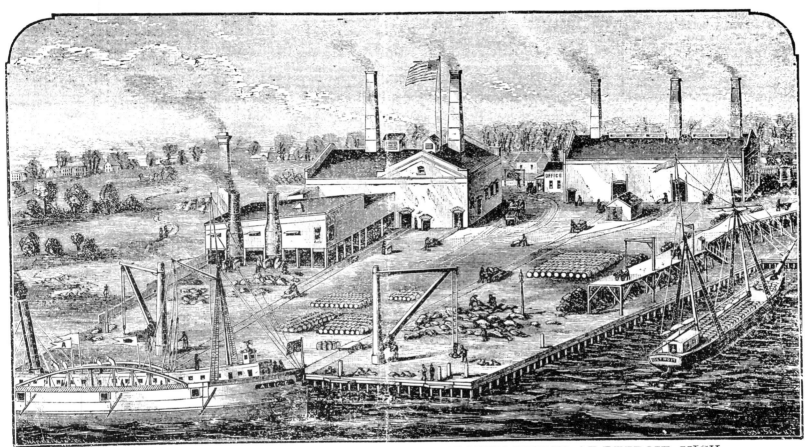

THE DETROIT AND LAKE SUPERIOR COPPER COMPANY'S WORKS AT DETROIT, MICH.

Cornish miners came from a tough school. This is a view of a copper-tin mine at St. Just, Cornwall, which was worked under the ocean for about a mile.

familiar with metals and was reluctant to believe the existence of pure copper in substantial amounts. John Hays, discoverer of the Cliff, shook their beliefs in the autumn of 1847 when he escorted a 4,000-pound copper mass to Liverpool, where it was exhibited. The *Liverpool Albion* was impressed enough to report that "it surpasses anything of the kind which we had supposed to exist." The *Albion* urged its readers to view the "curiosity" from the "inexhaustible mines of Lake Superior."[15]

All doubts regarding the amount and purity of Lake Superior copper were removed when the Cornish miners sent back reports from the Cliff to England. A few mining experts from Cornwall visited the Cliff in 1853 to inspect what a few years earlier had been called "Yankee inventions." There was no longer any skepticism: "Ten years ago John Bull never dreamed that he could be beat in anything, especially in copper."[16]

The size and purity of Lake Superior copper startled the world, but this new copper posed insoluble questions to the nation's refineries. One early decision that proved premature was to smelt the copper at the mine site, thus sending down from Lake Superior bar copper ready for the rolling mills. Professor James Hodge built a furnace for the Albion Copper Company on the Gratiot River in 1846, and the Suffolk Mining Company near Eagle River built a furnace in 1847. By the next year both furnaces were idle, due to breakdowns and lack of trained personnel.[17]

This was the era when the Cliff began spewing forth thousand-pound masses, and the Pittsburgh and Boston Mining Company needed an efficient, inexpensive, and fast smelting process. In 1846-47 they worked with the Revere Copper Works in Boston. Revere, though, charged approximately $80 a ton for smelting, and the Boston furnaces choked on the Lake Superior masses.[18]

Some of the Cliff copper was sent to the Baltimore and Cuba Smelting Works, where inexperience and other factors led to disastrous results. At Baltimore the masses were cut by hand labor into chunks of manageable proportions. Then the chunks were pulled across the floor by chains,

sufficient copper was in the furnace, the door was bricked up, and the furnace was charged. The method worked, but the whole operation was time-consuming, expensive, and damaging to the furnace hearths.[19]

Hussey was frustrated enough with the inadequacy of the Boston and Baltimore smelters to launch a series of experiments himself. In 1847 at the Fort Pitt foundry he used a cannon furnace for smelting of Cliff copper, but too much of the copper was lost in the slag (refuse) that was skimmed from the top. In this same year Hussey sent John Hays to England to inspect furnaces there, but the English managers did their best to conceal smelting methods and theories from Hays.[20]

In the late 1840s Hussey, as a result of testing and backed with slim reports from Hays about the furnaces in Wales, developed the reverberatory furnace, which revolutionized copper smelting and for the next 100 years was the method used throughout the United States. The principle was simple. The top of each furnace was movable; copper masses were lifted by crane and then lowered into the furnace, after which the top was replaced. The contents of the furnace were then brought to a melting point, at which time the slag was skimmed off by workmen pulling steel hoes across the top and dragging the molten slag through a small opening in the furnace. Then, huge hardwood logs were pushed into the molten copper; this got rid of the oxygen, because the carbon in the wood united with the oxygen in the copper and escaped as gas. The end result was copper that was usually 99 per cent pure. By 1850 the Hussey furnaces were in full operation, with around 100 Welsh workers on hand.[21]

Others soon adopted the Hussey smelting method, one of the first being his brother J. G. Hussey, who built a smelter in Cleveland in 1850. Like his brother in Pittsburgh, J. G. was also a pork and general food merchant, and he hoped to get much of the Lake Superior copper business. Over the years, though, he only got major orders for Cliff and National copper, both pretty much controlled by his brother. Finally, unable to compete with smelters in

Hussey's brother in Cleveland, J.G., had merchant and shipping contacts on Lake Superior.

John R. Grout

Pittsburgh and Detroit, the Cleveland works closed in 1867.[22]

Smelting experiments had been going on near Detroit since 1848, when the Smith Foundry at Birmingham produced its first pig of copper. This trial run was supervised by John R. Grout. He was unhappy with the result and decided to get backing from major brass firms in Connecticut. They were impressed with the potential of Detroit's location, and the result was the organization of the Detroit and Waterbury Copper Smelting Works in 1850. The Hussey furnace method was adopted in the Detroit works.[23]

After smelting, copper is milled and rolled, and Hussey decided that it made little sense to send smelted copper to other Eastern cities for these operations. Laughter and ridicule abounded when Hussey announced that Pittsburgh would be the milling center of the United States. In 1848-49 the C. G. Hussey Company was formed for the rolling of copper, and production was started on July 1850, at a mill on the Monongahela, a mile north of Pittsburgh. This was the first copper rolling mill west of the Alleghenies and the first in the country to supply American milled copper in large quantities.[24]

In true nineteenth century capitalistic fashion, Hussey next tackled the marketing of finished copper. At that time all copper was sold through a New York commission house, which Hussey distrusted because the New York people were too concerned with their foreign clients. Hussey built a sales warehouse near his Pittsburgh mills and was in business.[25] The various Hussey firms, then, by 1850 controlled all aspects of copper production in the country. His mine, the Cliff, was the leading producer, and his furnaces and mills in Pittsburgh were the best in the country; furthermore, he controlled the marketing from his Pittsburgh warehouse. His was the only complete copper empire of the era.[26]

The Hussey smelting and rolling works were moved and expanded in the late 1850s, and continued to be the nation's leader in these activities until the mid-1860s. In 1860 the Portage Lake Smelting Works were built in the Houghton-Hancock area to smelt Lake Superior copper on the spot. In 1867 the Detroit works combined with these works

and the result was the Detroit and Lake Superior Copper Company, with John Grout as general manager. One of the first clients for the new operation was the newly formed Calumet and Hecla Company, which was beginning to tap the rich amygdaloid and conglomerate lodes. By the late 1860s Cliff production had noticeably declined, so the Hussey smelting and milling works in Pittsburgh no longer had a complete empire; they had to buy copper from other Lake Superior mines.[27]

The Hussey name is still affixed to quality copper products, but after C. G. Hussey's death in 1893 inertia set in, and the firm suffered. His grandson, Curtis Grubb Hussey, Jr., was more interested in social life and big-game hunting in Africa. He died in 1924, but by that time the firm was controlled by Edward Hussey Binns. Although Binns

Hussey's copper rolling mill and smelter, Pittsburgh.

Interior view of a Pittsburgh rolling mill.

tried to revitalize the firm by borrowing half a million dollars from Pittsburgh banks, the Great Depression meant the end of corporate life. The firm was purchased by Copper Range Company of Boston and Michigan, but the name Hussey was retained. The Hussey Metals Division of Copper Range is located at Leetsdale, suburban Pittsburgh, and has one of North America's most modern copper rolling mills.[28]

The Hussey genius extended to the other great Pittsburgh industry, steel manufacturing. His name is associated with crucible steel manufacturing, and other than Sir Arthur Bessemer, Hussey was the foremost personality in steel innovations in the century. From the 1300s on, iron had been manufactured by blasting air through a combination of ore, flux, and charcoal. This cast iron was hard but very brittle. Wrought iron, an improvement, was formed in a forge by heating and hammering while fanned by bellows; it never becomes a liquid. Wrought iron is good iron and is never brittle, but only limited production was possible in this time-consuming process.[29]

Steel is iron with approximately 1 per cent carbon; the more carbon, the harder the steel. One early process was "cementation," where strips of wrought iron were heated white while packed in a cement of animal carbon and char-

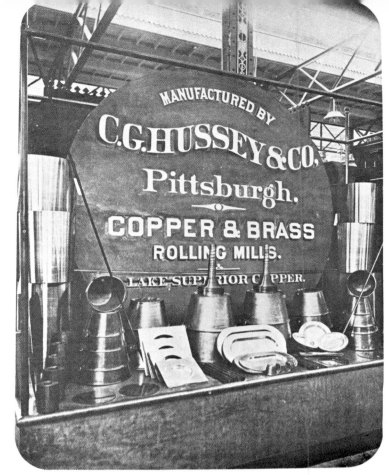

C. G. Hussey & Co. exhibits its wares in Philadelphia in 1876.

The modern rolling mill of Hussey Metals Division, Copper Range, Pittsburgh.

ortage Lake Copper Works in foreground; across the water is Houghton.

Steel works of Hussey, Wells & Company, when intense industrial smoke meant community pride.

coal; the iron absorbed the carbon. This, too, was a complicated, lengthy process.

The crucible process was invented by Huntsman in England in 1740. The steel was placed in a sealed pot (crucible) along with flux and other material, then placed in a furnace. The result was steel that had uniform properties throughout, rather than only on the exterior. The major disadvantages were the time involved, the cost of the crucibles, and the large amount of fuel used.

Western Pennsylvania had become a leading iron producer in the 1790s, and by 1800 there were eleven furnaces near Chestnut Ridge. This vicinity was ideal for iron products, because of the iron ore and limestone (flux) deposits, water power to operate the blast (by moving the bellows), a good network of rivers and roads, and vast stands of timber; an acre of timber a day was required to get enough charcoal for each furnace.[30]

By mid-century Pittsburgh was a sizable steel producer, the leading firm being McKelvy & Blair. They even imported English clay, trying to copy all aspects of English crucible steel manufacture, but the steel they made was a poor imitation.

Meanwhile, Hussey and banker Thomas Howe had accumulated a fortune from their copper enterprises and decided to develop a steel process superior to the English. Politics played a key part in the decision, for Hussey and Howe felt that the new Republican party, to which they belonged, would come out for a strong protective tariff. If so, English crucible steel would be banned, and there would be room for a major domestic producer.

Calvin Wells, a Hussey merchant-associate since 1850, was brought into the scheme, and Hussey bought out the Pittsburgh firm of Blair & Company. The firm of Hussey, Wells, & Co., was formed in 1859, with production beginning at a plant at 17th and Penn Streets in 1860. The "direct process" method developed by Hussey consisted of transmitting the heat speedily from the furnace to the white-hot crucible. The main advantage of the process, in addition to its speed, was that the crucibles could be used over and over, thus saving thousands of dollars. The three-acre site near downtown Pittsburgh included, in addition to the furnaces, rolling mills, hammer mills, and melting shops. Eight steam engines provided all the power. By the mid-1860s the firm was producing twenty tons of finished steel a day, and the company's cast crucible steel was "warrented to be equal to the best English steel."[31] The reason for the success, according to one biographer, was that while facing a difficult decision, Hussey "threw his Anglo-Saxon grit into the balance."[32]

The firm grew rapidly and by 1870 had over fifty furnaces operating. Wells bowed out of the business to go into publishing, and the firm was renamed Hussey, Howe & Co.

In 1863 Hussey had visited the Peabody & Co. works in England, which had adopted the Bessemer method of steel production. Hussey was offered American rights for the Bessemer process but turned the offer down, citing problems of financial risk and large number of workers needed for the process. This, supposedly, was the sole business mistake Hussey ever made.[33]

The Hussey steel story has been treated here in some detail because it shows part of the use to which the rich profits of the Cliff were put. Also, it is clear from this steel narrative that the Hussey success with the Cliff was no fluke. He was a shrewd investor and entrepreneur who acted on the basis of thorough investigation, backed by an awareness of a need. One biographer made a claim for Hussey that was repeated over the years: "If his lot had been cast in Wall Street, he would have been one of its Kings."[34]

The men who controlled the Pittsburgh and Boston Mining Company had somewhat different backgrounds, but once the profits piled up they acted with marked similarity in making new investments and spending on charitable works. These men were financial giants of the era, and their stories reveal much of the capitalistic philosophy that ruled the day.

The originator of the Lake Superior venture was Curtis Grubb Hussey, who was born in August 11, 1802, on a farm near York, Pa. His father was Christopher Hussey, whose origins in New England went back to 1630; the first Christopher Hussey was a representative in the General Court of Massachusetts Sessions.[35]

The Hussey family moved to a farm near Mt. Pleasant, Ohio, and Curtis studied medicine there with a local physician. He was licensed to practice in 1825 and moved at that time to Morgan County, Indiana. He soon owned several stores and other businesses, and he developed an extensive pork shipping network from Indiana towns. His reputation was such that he was elected to the Indiana state legislature in 1829 but declined a second term.[36]

Hussey married Rebecca Updegraff of Jefferson County, Ohio, in 1839 and moved to Pittsburgh in that year; Pitts-

Investment, invention, travel, and philanthropy characterized Hussey's activities after the Cliff bonanza occurred. In addition to the copper and steel centers he controlled in Pittsburgh, he also had substantial investments in ten other Lake Superior mines, traveled to California and the Rocky Mountains to inspect and invest, and controlled much of what went on in several Pittsburgh banks.[38]

During his lifetime Hussey accumulated between ten and twenty million dollars, and he spent lavishly on educational institutions. He purchased a tract of land near Pittsburgh which he donated for the Allegheny Observatory; he also bought much of the expensive equipment for this nationally famous institution and served as its president for years. He was also a founder of the Pittsburgh School of Design for Women, serving as its first president in 1865. Hussey also contributed thousands of dollars to such varied institutions as the schools in Indian Territory, Wesleyan College for Women in Cincinnati, and Earlham College in Indiana. One project that especially pleased him was the Hussey School for Girls in Matamoras, Mexico. A prominent Pittsburgh Quaker, Hussey vigorously supported and contributed to abolitionist, antislavery, and abstinence movements.[39]

Curtis G. Hussey, the dominant personality in the Pittsburgh and Boston operations.

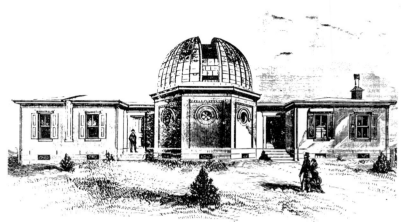

Allegheny Observatory, financed from Lake Superior copper.

burgh was the main link for Hussey's pork shipments to the East.[37] A few years later Hussey became fascinated with the Lake Superior copper news outlined earlier in these pages.

The Hussey involvement in business and education did not lead to an active social life. He was "quiet and retiring" and preferred seclusion and conference rather than public notice.[40] The Hussey family had three daughters and two sons; Christopher Curtis Hussey worked in the various family firms until his early death in 1884. His son, Curtis Grubb Hussey, Jr., was prominent in social circles, Pennsylvania National Guard politics, and big-game hunting. He had some connections with the various Hussey enterprises but never distinguished himself like his namesake. He died in Pittsburgh in 1924.[41]

The man who delivered the funds when the Cliff was in desperate need in the late 1840s was also a Pittsburgh resident, the Reverend Charles Avery. He was born in Westchester County, New York, in 1784 and settled in Pittsburgh as a drug merchant in 1812. Avery also developed interests in Southern cotton, and during his trips there he came an active antislavery advocate. By the 1840s, when Avery made his great financial stake in the Cliff, he was one of Pittsburgh's solid citizens. He had been trained to be a Methodist preacher, and although most of his life he was not a practicing clergyman, he was frequently known as a "local preacher."[42]

After 1849, when Pittsburgh and Boston Mining Company dividends began to flood Pittsburgh, Avery went on a philanthropic spree that set the pattern for the other Cliff owners. He built several churches in Pittsburgh and Allegheny City and contributed time and money towards setting up an efficient Underground Railroad system. Confident that Negroes could excel in all endeavors, Avery became founder and president of Avery College in Allegheny City. This was the first chartered Negro college in the country.[43]

Avery money was donated to such varied causes as the Preacher's Aid Society, Oberlin College, American Missionary Society, Allegheny Institute, and several Methodist minister funds. Avery and his wife, the former Martha Bryan of New York State, were childless. When Avery died on January 17, 1858, he left an estate of $800,000, half of which went for Negro schools in the United States and for

Reverend Charles Avery.

Avery's elaborate tomb in Allegheny Cemetery, Pittsburgh.

spreading Christianity "among the benighted black and colored races...of Africa." He was buried in Allegheny Cemetery in an ornately-sculptured tomb by Louis Verhagen of New York. The Italian-marble statue of Avery on top of the tomb was twenty-four feet high and was said to be pointed "as bound for Africa."[44]

References to Avery in twentieth century accounts usually ignore his investments in Lake Superior copper. His philanthropy is praised, his antislavery work admired, and his contributions toward Negro education are fondly remembered. Yet, this provincial, Pittsburgh-oriented view distorts Avery's role, for without his timely investment in Cliff copper, his many humanitarian works would not have been possible.[45]

Banker Thomas Marshall Howe was the third major Pittsburgh figure in these copper-iron investments, and he, too, was of solid Yankee stock. He was born in Williamston, Vermont, in 1808, a direct descendant of John Howe who had settled in Massachusetts in 1638. The Howe family moved from Vermont to a farm near Bloomfield, Ohio, in 1817. Thomas went to the local academy and in 1829 he went to Pittsburgh, where for the next decade he worked in drygoods and hardware establishments. He became a partner in the hardware firm of Leavitt & Co. in the early 1830s.[46]

In the late 1830s Howe switched to banking and was appointed cashier of the Pittsburgh Exchange Bank in 1838. It was as cashier that Howe became familiar with Hussey, Avery, and other Pittsburgh businessmen. When Hussey invested in Lake Superior copper in 1843 it was on the advice of Howe; and it was Howe who in 1847 served as advisor to Avery when the major investment was made that turned the Cliff from a romantic dream to a successful mine. Until his death in 1877 Howe was linked with Hussey in most copper and steel ventures, not only in Pittsburgh but in the mines of Lake Superior and the Rocky Mountains.[47]

Howe's contributions to the Hussey success were as a financial mastermind and business leader, not as a mining or steel expert. Cliff dividends meant a personal fortune for Howe, and in 1851 he became president of the Exchange Bank. In the following years the firm of Hussey, Howe & Co. (under various names) controlled all of the copper and much of the quality steel production of Pittsburgh. Howe's reputation in business circles led to his election as the first president of the Pittsburgh Chamber of Commerce. His ability to foresee events and needs was well known to his associates; he was one of the founders of the Cleveland and Pittsburgh Railway and served as treasurer of the Monongahela Navigation Company.[48]

Thomas M. Howe.

Politics for Howe meant an opportunity to protect his business interests and to join with antislavery forces, a position he shared with colleagues Hussey and Avery. In 1851-55 he served as a Whig in the United States Congress. He returned to his business pursuits, but the new Republican party received much aid from him. He was a delegate to the Republican National Convention in Chicago in 1860 and was a presidential elector on the Republican ticket which selected Lincoln and Hamlin in that year.[49]

At the beginning of the Civil War, Howe vigorously supported Lincoln's policies. He became Assistant Adjutant General of Pennsylvania and did much to recruit and train the dozens of Union regiments raised in the state. In later years he was frequently referred to as General Howe because of these wartime contributions.[50]

Howe's philanthropic activities were not so extensive as Hussey's, nor so inspired as Avery's. He did, though, actively support the Allegheny Observatory for years and served as a trustee. He was one of the founders of the exclusive Allegheny Cemetery, and after Avery's death in 1858, Howe served as president of the cemetery board for the next twenty years. He was also a member of Trinity Church for thirty years and was a founder and warden of Cavalry Church. Howe died in July of 1877 and was buried in Allegheny Cemetery.[51]

Investments, whether they be conservative or speculative, demand money. Business leaders in cities nearest the copper fields—Detroit and Cleveland—did not at first rush to buy stocks in the new Lake Superior copper mines. Instead, most financing came from established companies and wealthy individuals in the Eastern cities of Boston, New York, Philadelphia, and Pittsburgh.

The Hussey-Howe combination was first on the scene, but close behind were the finances controlled by Horatio Bigelow and Joseph Clark of Boston, who after a few years dominated more than fifteen companies. In his fine work entitled *Michigan Copper and Boston Dollars*, William Gates ironically does not investigate why Boston money was so quick on the scene and dominated the copper mar-

Rodolphe L. Agassiz,
first president of Calumet and Hecla.

ket after the demise of the Cliff. All Gates can offer is a footnote which claims that the Boston control was "something of a mystery." He records two theories: one, that Boston had received the background and interest in copper by earlier investments in the Nova Scotia mines; and two,

that Bostonian David Henshaw, Secretary of the Navy, became so interested in Lake Superior prospects that he resigned his cabinet post and with his Boston friends invested in new copper mines.[52]

Gates and others have ignored the role of Charles T. Jackson, prominent Boston scientist and U. S. Surveyor who explored the lands several times in the late 1840s and wrote extensively of his findings. Jackson and his fellow-surveyors, John W. Foster and J. D. Whitney, explored privately for Boston-financed groups. Jackson returned to Boston in the winters and had much influence in high social and financial circles.

As early as the summer of 1844, Henshaw, "one of the richest stockholders" in the Lake Superior Company, personally visited the tract near Eagle River in company with "Mr. Jackson, the great Geologist of Boston." In later years, because of the involvement of men like Quincy Shaw and R. L. Agassiz, Boston financiers dominated the Calumet & Hecla Mining Company. Much local Lake Superior lore has grown about Boston riches derived from lake copper, but at best this is a provincial point of view. As Frederic C. Jaher has pointed out in a recent study, the bluebloods of Boston were more established in railroads than in copper. A more accurate assessment for this era is that from 1845 to 1865 the fortunes of Lake Superior copper were more closely linked with the financial-industrial center of Pittsburgh; after Calumet & Hecla began in the 1860s, Boston supplanted Pittsburgh as the center of copper activity.[53]

Part of the copper history lore is the oft-repeated statement that the Hussey-led Pittsburgh investors were tight-fisted conservatives who abhorred speculation. Gates mentioned this characteristic and said that compared to the Boston group the Hussey forces "were much more circumspect in their operations."[54]

The Pittsburgh people helped to shape this image. In the annual report for 1862 Hussey spent several paragraphs explaining how the mining firm went to great lengths to avoid speculation.[55] In his own time Hussey was praised as being so conservative in his investments that he never borrowed money.[56] The same was said for Reverend Avery: "His wealth was all amassed in an honorable and legitimate manner. Speculation was not to his taste, and greedy self-seeking speculators he abhorred."[57]

Yet, an examination of the record proves otherwise. That Hussey never borrowed money may be true, but in that fateful winter meeting of 1847, Hussey and Howe put the pressure on Avery to sink $80,000 in the Cliff venture. And what few people know is that the Pittsburgh group invested heavily and controlled more than a dozen other Lake Superior mining companies, most of which produced dismal records.

Hussey, Howe, or Avery were officers in the following firms: North Western Mining Company, Mass Mining Company, Great Western Mining Company, Miscowaubik Mining Company, Aztec Mining Company, Copper Harbor Mining Company, Mann Mining Company, Swamscott Mining Company, National Mining Company, Adventure Mining Company, and the Central Mining Company. Some of these firms were as speculative as the names imply. Only the Central and National were consistent money-makers. The other firms had unsuccessful or mediocre records.[58]

That the Hussey philosophy was far from conservative can also be seen by studying the investment record of his brother Joseph, headquartered in Cleveland. In 1850 Joseph began his copper smelting works there, but he continued to act as shipping agent for several Lake Superior lines, and with W. D. McBride he operated a merchant agency to supply flour, pork, fish, salt, lime, and other goods to the Lake Superior copper camps. Joseph also invested heavily in the speculative Copper Harbor Mining Company.[59]

Success at the Cliff led the Hussey-Howe team to investigate other North American properties. As early as 1849 Hussey traveled to California and invested in gold properties. In later years he went to British Columbia, the Rocky Mountains, and Georgia, investing along the way but not

Hussey and Howe invested in silver lands in Clear Creek County, Colorado, in 1871.

striking anything that resembled the Cliff riches. By the late 1860s Hussey controlled three silver mines in Mexico. These were bad investments, but the success at the Cliff seems to have caused Hussey to hope for more of the same; as late as 1871 he and Howe bought several silver properties on the U. S. Grant Lode in Clear Creek County, Colorado.[60]

The Pittsburgh investments in mining firms, aside from the Cliff, were as erratic as Horace Greeley had predicted back in 1847. Yet, in the business and industrial developments in western Pennsylvania, the Hussey-Howe group delivered a Midas record. And, aside from their financial success, they also encouraged and contributed to major technological advances.

When Andrew Carnegie arrived in this country from Scotland in 1845, Hussey, Howe, and Avery were already embarked on their metal-oriented careers. By the turn of the century, when steel-giant Carnegie was contributing millions to charitable and educational institutions, most people had forgotten that he was only following the pattern of Hussey, Howe, and Avery. These men, long before any "Robber Baron" complex had stirred capitalist consciences, had contributed to a variety of schools, churches, cemeteries, libraries, orphanages, and observatories, not only in Pittsburgh but in many other places in the United States and Mexico.

One of the few sad notes in the Pittsburgh and Boston Mining Company story is that the discoverer of the Cliff Mine, John Hays, failed to share in its profits. After his smelter-inspecting tour of England, Hays helped Hussey set up the new furnaces in Pittsburgh in 1848. He was superintendent of the operation for the next two years. Following a disagreement with Hussey in 1850, Hays went to Cleveland where he was associated with coal mining and distributing companies. He lived there until his death in April of 1901.[61]

1. The Sault newspaper reported most shipments, including name of boat and captain, weight of cargo, destination, and sometimes names of passengers. See for example the *Lake Superior News and Mining Journal*, September 25, 1847, reporting the arrival of the schooner "Napoleon."

2. Laurence Oliphant, *Minnesota and the Far West* (Edinburgh: William Blackwood & Sons, 1855), p. 103.

3. *Lake Superior News and Mining Journal*, August 18, 1848. For an excellent account of the canal under construction, and the railway in use, see *Inland Seas*, XXIV (Summer 1968), which reprints an illustrated article from *Ballou's Pictorial Drawing-Room Companion*, XII (May 9, 1857).

4. Oliphant, *Minnesota and the Far West*, p. 103.

5. For St. Lusson see a memoir to the King of France, November 2, 1671, in *New York Colonial Documents*, IX (1855), 71-73. For building of Ft. Brady, see Henry Schoolcraft to Governor Cass, July 12, 1822, Records of the Michigan Superintendency of Indian Affairs, Letters Received, Reel 113, pp. 47-49.

6. In 1797 the North West Company of fur traders built a small, crude lock for larger batteaux on the Canadian side of the river.

7. Clark Norton, "Early Movement for the St. Mary's Falls Ship Canal," *Michigan History*, XXXIX (September, 1955), 257-80.

8. Summarized from Irene D. Neu, "The Building of the Sault Canal: 1852-1855," *Mississippi Valley Historical Review*, XL (June, 1953), 25-46.

9. A good summary of the canal building is in F. Clever Bald, *Michigan in Four Centuries* (New York: Harper & Bros., 1961), pp. 243-45. For "Iron City" see George A. Marr, "Captain George Perry McKay," *Inland Seas*, XXII (Fall, 1966), 208-25.

10. Issue of June 26, 1850.

11. *Mining Magazine*, VII (1856), 311.

12. These stories were reprinted in the *Lake Superior Journal*, September 25, 1847, and June 11, 1851.

13. *Lake Superior News and Miners' Journal* (Copper Harbor), October 3, 1846; for a typical report of shipments to France, see *Mining Magazine*, IV (March, 1855), 175.

14. Some of the material was reprinted as *Voyage au Lac Superieur* (Paris: Victor Dalmont, 1855).

15. The *Albion* article was reprinted in *Lake Superior News and Mining Journal*, October 30, 1847.

16. *Lake Superior Journal*, August 6, 1853.

17. Alvah L. Sawyer, *A History of the Northern Peninsula of Michigan* (Chicago: Lewis Publ. Co., 1911), I, 277.

18. An unsigned biography of Hussey appears in *Magazine of Western History*, III (February, 1886), 238-39.

19. James B. Cooper, "Historical Sketch of Smelting and Refining Lake Copper," *Proceedings of the Lake Superior Mining Institute*, VII (1901), 44-49. Cooper and his father were smelter superintendents in Detroit and Portage Lake.

20. For Ft. Pitt experiments see *Magazine of Western History*, III (February, 1886), 238-29. For Hays' trip to England see Williams, *The Honorable Peter White*, pp. 9-16.

21. *History of Allegheny County, Pennsylvania* (Philadelphia: L. H. Everts & Co., 1876), p.116; *Magazine of Western History*, III (February, 1886), 238-39; Gates; *Michigan Copper and Boston Dollars*, p. 29. This method remained unchanged until recent years. In the early 1950s I worked as a smelter hand for Calumet & Hecla, and the operation was the same as that devised by Hussey in the late 1840s.

22. Cooper, *Proceedings of the Lake Superior Mining Institute*, VII (1901), p. 45.

23. *Ibid.*, see also *Mining Magazine*, I (1853), 298; *Detroit Free Press*, July 15, 1848, for first smelting in Detroit.

24. Mentioned in Hussey obituary, *Pittsbirgh Dispatch*, April 26, 1893; *Dictionary of American Biography*, IX, 431.

25. *Magazine of Western History*, III (February, 1886), 339; *History of Allegheny County, Pennsylvania* (Chicago: A. Warner & Co., 1889), II, 254-58.

26. Leander Bishop in 1868 praised the Hussey works, calling them the "first establishment projected for working exclusively American Copper"; *A History of American Manufactures from 1608 to 1860* (Philadelphia: Edward Young & Co., 1868), III, 107.

27. Summarized from Cooper, *Proceedings of the Lake Superior Mining Institute*, VII (1901), pp. 45-48.

28. *Bulletin Index* (Pittsburgh), December 17, 1936, for an article on the Hussey copper works. The parent company devoted an entire issue of their magazine to the Hussey Metals Division; see *Copper Range News*, IV (1964).

29. This, and much of the crucible steel information that follows, is from Harrison Gilmer, "Birth of the American Crucible Steel Industry," *Western Pennsylvania Historical Magazine*, XXXVI (March, 1953), 17-36. I am indebted to Frank A. Zabrosky of the Archives of Industrial Society, University of Pittsburgh, for bringing this article to my attention.

30. This paragraph is based on an excellent iron-making exhibit in the Fort Pitt Museum, Pittsburgh.

31. Bishop, *History of American Manufacturers*, III, 108.

32. *History of Allegheny County* (1889), p. 256.

33. *Ibid.*, this is also mentioned in *Pittsburgh Dispatch*, April 23, 1893.

34. *Copper Range News*, IV (1964), 4. The Hussey steel works was purchased in 1918 by Universal Steel and was later absorbed by Cyclops Steel of Titusville, Pa.; *Bulletin Index* (Pittsburgh), December 17, 1936.

35. Hussey Genealogical Chart, Carnegie Library, Pittsburgh.

36. *Dictionary of American Biography*, IX, 430-31; *Magazine of Western History*, III (February, 1886), 332-33.

37. *History of Allegheny County* (1889), II, 254.

38. Mentioned in obituary in *Pittsburgh Dispatch*, April 26, 1893.

39. The best summary of these activities is in *History of Allegheny County* (1889), II, 257-58. See also *Pittsburgh and the Vicinity* (Boston: Biographical Review Publishing Co., 1897), XXIV, 506-07.

40. *Magazine of Western History*, III (February, 1886), 347.

41. Hussey Genealogical Chart, Carnegie Library, Pittsburgh.

42. An excellent biography of Avery, including two illustrations, is in *People's Monthly* (Pittsburgh), I (July, 1871), 15.

43. *Ibid*. See also a biographical article on Avery in the *Pittsburgh Post-Gazette*, March 25, 1954.

44. Obituaries in the *Lansing Republican* (Michigan), February 7, 1858, and *Pittsburgh Dispatch*, January 19, 1858. For a view of the tomb and a lengthy biography of Avery see *History of Allegheny County* (1876), p. 127.

45. Three recent articles on Avery are excellent for tracing his charities but are ignorant of the origin of his wealth; *Pittsburgh Press*, March 15, 1953; *Pittsburgh Post-Gazette*, March 25, 1954; *Pittsburgh Press*, Sunday Section, February 16, 1969.

46. Howe biographical file, Carnegie Library, Pittsburgh; a biography of Howe is in *Magazine of Western History*, II (October, 1885), 550-56.

47. A good biography of Howe is in *History of Allegheny County* (1889)' II, 262-63.

48. *Ibid*. See also *Thirteenth Annual Report of the President and Managers to the Monongahela Navigation Company* (1853), copy in the Carnegie Library, Pittsburgh.

49. *Biographical Directory of the American Congress, 1774-1961* (Washington: Government Printing Office, 1961), p. 1084.

50. *Magazine of Western History*, II (October, 1885), 550-56.

51. *Ibid*. See also *People's Monthly* (Pittsburgh), I (September, 1871), 57, for Allegheny Observatory; *Allegheny Cemetery: Historical Account* (Pittsburgh: Bakewell & Marthens, 1873), lists the founders and officers. Howe had a brother, William H., who followed him to Pittsburgh and later worked as a supervisor at the Cliff Mine. For an obituary of William, see *Portage Lake Mining Gazette*, March 4, 1886.

52. Gates, *Michigan Copper and Boston Dollars*, pp. 33-40, and footnote 123, p. 239.

53. Jackson's most ambitious report is in U.S. Congress, House, *Message From the President of the United States*, 31st Cong., 1st Sess., Ex. Doc. No. 5, Part III, 1849. His influence was such that copper mining articles by him were printed in the *American Journal of Science* (1846 and 1849); *Annales des Mines* (1850); *Comptes Rendus* (1854 and 1869). A conservative estimate would be that Jackson published copper mining accounts in six government documents, nine foreign journals, and at least a score of domestic scientific and popular magazines. For the Henshaw-Jackson visit to Lake Superior, see *Democratic Free Press* (Detroit), September 28, 1844. For Boston role see Frederic Cople Jaher, "The Boston Brahmins in the Age of Industrial Capitalism," *The Age of Industrialism in America* (New York: Free Press, 1968), p. 232.

54. Gates, *Michigan Copper and Boston Dollars*, p. 37.

55. The annual report is in *Portage Lake Mining Gazette*, May 23, 1863.

56. *Contemporary American Biography* (New York: Atlantic Publ. & Engraving Co., 1892), Part 2, p. 93.

57. *History of Allegheny County* (1876), p. 127.

58. A near-complete set of manuscript annual reports for these and dozens of other mining companies are in the Michigan State Archives.

59. A typical Hussey-McBride advertisement is in the *Lake Superior Miner* (Ontonagon), August 29, 1857. The articles of association for the Copper Harbor Mining Company, 1853, are in the Michigan State Archives.

60. Some of his investment history is in the *History of Allegheny County* (1889), p. 257. For mention of Mexican holdings see *Portage Lake Mining Gazette*, March 17, 1866. The deeds for the Colorado properties are in the Carnegie Library, Pittsburgh.

61. A chapter is devoted to Hays in Williams, *The Honorable Peter White*, pp. 9-16. There are two Hays newspaper obituaries in the Brockway Papers, University of Michigan Historical Collections.

Chapter 5:

Community Life

THE COPPER WAS MINED AND SHIPPED, but the community that developed around these activities represented something new on the American frontier—a mining town. Many of the conditions at Clifton were to be found later in the California, Montana, and Rocky Mountain towns, but the Cliff influence spread to all Lake Superior mining villages, and by the turn of the century there was not a mining town in the United States that lacked residents from the mining communities of northern Michigan.

Certainly there had been other mining communities in the United States before the development of Clifton in the mid-1840s. Copper, lead, coal, and other minerals were mined in the New England states, Georgia, Pennsylvania, Wisconsin, Illinois, Iowa, and other places, yet the system of permits, leases, and the concepts of military protection and Mineral Land Office set-up were first put into substantial use in the Lake Superior district. In 1843 in the Illinois courts the system of mining leases was considered in the case of the *United States* v. *H. H. Gear.* In this same year the Mineral Land Agency was created at Copper Harbor, and in the following year Fort Wilkins was established there.

The whole concept of leasing was revised, and the Secretary of War, J. M. Porter, saw fit to appoint General Walter Cunningham to run the new U. S. Mineral Land Agency at Copper Harbor. Cunningham had served in a similar capacity in the Galena, Illinois, lead region, and Porter wrote that: "The fidelity with which you have executed the duties . . . has induced me to continue your appointment and enlarge the sphere of your action." Cunningham was to maintain offices in Galena, but he was to work in Copper Harbor with the new leasing system until the Land Agency there was going smoothly. Therefore, the Lake Superior lands were the first to be developed under the new federal mining system, and the mining methods devised for the Lake Superior copper fields were to be followed closely in subsequent copper, iron, and other mining developments in the West.[1]

In the forefront of all levels of community life were

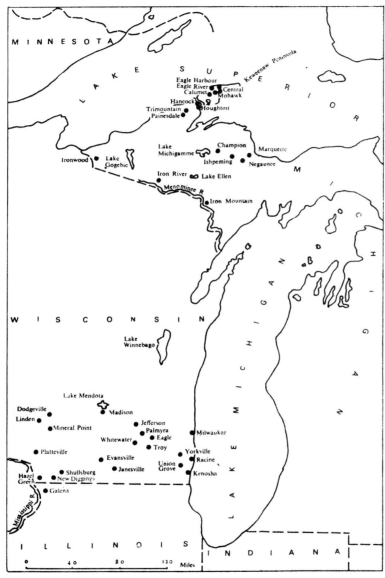

This map from Todd's book shows the main Cornish mining communities in Michigan and Wisconsin.

Cornishmen, and because they were to dominate nine-teenth century mining in this country, it is worth noting the reasons for this prominence. Fortunately, two Cornish authors have recently published books about the Cornish settlements in the New World.

Cornwall is a Celtic section of Great Britain, situated at the southwestern end of England. For centuries this region was famous for mining tin and copper, so that early in the nineteenth century the region was world-famous for production and for understanding of mining practices. By the middle of the century, though, the mines were too deep to be worked profitably. From the first word of the opening of the Lake Superior copper fields, Cornishmen were on hand. And if another man were needed, why not send for "Cousin Jack" back in Cornwall. The nickname stayed, and so did the Cornishmen. They brought to the New World a fierce pride in the mining profession; a strong, loud Methodism; a democratic, independent streak that would later horrify union organizers; modestly educated but upward-striving citizens that would be pace-setters in any community.

Ethnic generalities are tough to make, but Rowse, Todd, and others generally agree that mining dominated the Cornish personality to such an extent that little of significance in the arts or letters has ever come out of Cornwall. Even in the world of business Cornishmen did not rise to the top, though they often dominated the middle management layers. In the United States the Cousin Jack became *the* mining captain, boss, foreman, and so forth. The typical lad in Cornwall knew something about mining before he was ten years old, so when Cornishmen came to America they had a built-in advantage over the multitudes from other parts of Europe. Add to this the Cornish personality which consisted of self-assurance and independence, and we have the makings of a boss class. This they became, from the Wisconsin lead mines to the Lake Superior copper and iron mines to the rich lodes of California and the Rockies. Dozens of nationalities joined the laboring crews on the mining frontier, but it was unthinkable for a Pascoe,

The Cornish mining captain is wearing white clothes, the status symbol of the depths.

Some early Keweenaw miners.

Trevillian, Trevaskis, Tremaine, Penberthy, or Penrose to be anything except a boss to the various Finns, Italians, Germans, and Slavs in the mining crews. Let us look, then, at the first large Cornish mining village in the New World.

By 1850, after five years of working at the Cliff, the population of about 500 consisted primarily of Cornishmen, with some Irishmen, Germans, and French Canadians. Like any frontier, the Cliff attracted young, single males, and most of them took room and board at company-owned houses. These were boisterous years, and the boarding houses were busy and dirty. Because the miners worked in shifts, three different men might use the same bed in one twenty-four-hour period. The typical boarding house contained a kitchen plus sleeping room, large enough to handle thirty to forty men. Drinking and card playing were the only entertainment in the early years, and fist fights and wrestling matches between Cornish and Irish were common.[2]

The company wanted to have a permanent labor supply, so one of the magnets was to provide housing at a nominal fee. For example, the typical miner on the Keweenaw earned $34 monthly in 1853, and one-fourth to one-half of this went for room and board. This left a comfortable margin for whiskey, gambling, or a fund to bring "Cousin Jack." Up to around 1860 most men lived in company-owned boarding houses operated by a middle-aged woman, usually a widow with a built-in work force of two or three children. The company sold land at a reasonable price to miners who wished to build homes.[3]

The first "dignified" lady at the Cliff was the wife of John Hays, discoverer of the Cliff lode. Hays married Susan Sterling of Pittsburgh in 1846 and took her at once to live in the bleak accommodations at the Cliff.[4]

Medical care was provided from the beginning by a company physician. Soon the "bal surgeon" system of health insurance was everywhere, based on the system in use in Cornwall. Each worker contributed a small monthly sum to the company doctor, who then was responsible for treating the entire family. The precambrian geology of Lake Superior meant that the shaft walls were so solid that cave-ins were rare, and bad gases were practically unknown in the mines. Yet, there were many underground accidents that maimed or killed workers. Blasting was always dangerous, as was the tremendous challenge of climbing or descending 1,000 feet of ladders. Winters on Lake Superior are cold and snowy, and sniffles, flues, etc., kept the doctors busy. A doctor's talents were also needed after a bloody Cornish-Irish Saturday night brawl in nearby Eagle River.[5]

One time in the early years the Rev. Eri H. Day, local Methodist clergyman, was going down in the mine and at the 400 foot level tripped over a cussing man whose foot was trapped under a two-ton rock. The man had been too close to an explosion. The Reverend also helped the physician fix the skull of a man caught in the classic mine accident: the miner lit a fuse, hid behind a rock, and waited. Nothing happened, so the man raised his head to look and the blast went off, tore his hat to shreds, scattered bits of rock all over his face, and broke his skull and arm.[6]

The "bal surgeon" was only one of many Cornish terms that was soon commonly used on the mining frontier. "Bal" is the Cornish word for "mine." Other such words from this dialect that made their way into American mining talk included "deads" meaning waste rock; "mad water" for water that seeped back into the mines; "bravely keenly lode" for a particularly rich strike. C. H. Vivian refers to these Cornish mining terms as "crake." He gives the following "crake" example for describing a mine:

It had a hore body that must be got hout of the ground. It might have a west hend and a heast hend and perhaps a blue stope and a 'ard hore stope.

"Crake" also meant that personal pronouns were applied to inanimate objects. Thus, a shovel was a he or she, never an "it."[7]

This remote village of Clifton needed food, and from the beginning the company encouraged farming. By 1848 twenty-five acres were being farmed, mostly hay for the horses and mules and vegetables for the inhabitants. The company bragged about its imposing little village of 300, with a physician, preacher, and schoolmaster.[8] The *Lake Superior Journal* expressed well the interest in farming at Clifton: "True, as farming country this is not great, but mines need produce, and they can pay."[9]

In 1856 the *Mining Magazine* of New York pointed to Clifton as a model village, with many new dwellings, a new road, and a new church being planned. Each of the new houses had a small garden plot.

How pleasant it is to see taste and comfort consulted in the arrangement of our mining locations . . . . We would like to see the agents, in laying out of villages or location lots, leave a reasonable garden for each house . . . . Men who have spent long hours several hundred feet below the reach of sunshine must have recreation. And many who now become disorderly would not frequent the bar-room if they had a garden to cultivate or a comfortable house to bring themselves about.[10]

The gardening and farming increased remarkably for this rocky soil, and in 1860 the company grew 200 tons of hay and 500 bushels of oats.[11] This crop was solely for the horses, mules, and oxen which were used in moving copper, timbers, and mining equipment between Eagle River and Clifton.

Law and order at the Cliff was kept by rigid company discipline, with the help of the sheriff and occasional deputies from Eagle River. Most of the problems were related to whiskey. Even as early as 1846 an enterprising peddler set up a saloon near the Cliff, but John Hays supposedly explained to the men the evils of whiskey, so they would not patronize the place.[12] Hays' success is most likely exaggerated, as alcohol was a constant problem.

The company did much to discourage the use of whiskey, not out of hatred for sin alcohol, but drinking usually led to brawling confrontations between Cornishmen and Irishmen. Wounded miners did not mine well.[13] Drinking was also a pleasant way of celebrating. In one account a reporter joined three men from the Cliff who were just returning from their first trip to Portage Lake, twenty miles to the south. "Two Cornishmen amused us very much by their antics and expressions, they 'being well filled with the 'essence of Pike.' "[14]

It is impossible to exaggerate the bitterness between the Irishmen and Cornishmen during this era. The Methodist, hymn-singing Cornishmen had nothing but contempt for the Catholic Irish who did most of the menial tasks in the mine and on the surface. Whiskey consumed meant battle lines drawn, and after a few broken noses and wrecked buildings, a motley bi-national crew would spend the night in the Eagle River jail.

The bitterness extended over the entire mining region. A famous battle with guns, clubs, and knives took place on the Ontonagon range between these two groups in early 1859. Another example of the severity of these acts occurred in Hancock a few years later when a Cornishman, quietly smoking his pipe while walking home from the Quincy Mine, was assaulted and stabbed five times by a gang of thirteen Irishmen. The newspaper expressed pleasant surprise when the Irish sheriff, Ed Ryan, actually arrested the Irish ruffians.[15]

For another example of legal problems we have the William Crase affair. The *Gazette* published an account of how Crase, through a pay error, received $300 too much from the Cliff clerk. He took the money, "lit out" for Hancock, where he was arrested. On the way back to Clifton, Crase managed to escape. The Cliff clerk, R. Updegraff, wrote a sarcastic letter to the *Gazette*, explaining that Crase was not a Robin Hood, nor was he over-paid:

> A man by the name of Wm. H. Crase run his contract and left his board and washing unpaid. We thought to make an example of him, but it appears that on their way back he was overtaken by the old thirst for the more genial atmosphere of Hancock.[16]

The Cliff like other Lake Superior communities was not riddled with serious crimes. Yet, there were occasional robberies, murders, and rapes. One particular crime in 1863 is interesting because many aspects of mining community life were present in the case.

A man named Harris ran a boarding house at the Cliff, and he also worked night shift in the mine. A blacksmith named Richards had formerly stayed in the Harris boarding house, but he was asked to leave when he became overly friendly with Mrs. Harris. Yet, from time to time Richards would sneak over to visit Mrs. Harris at night, while Harris was 500 feet underground. After some time gossip got around, and even the mine captains urged Richards to end these nocturnal visits. Harris was even told of this by his wife, who apparently delighted in annoying him by talking about Richards.

Harris decided to act, so he bought a double-barreled shotgun, hid it just under the stairway, and left for work. He sneaked back to the house, heard voices, then smashed down the locked door with an axe. Richards and Mrs. Harris were sitting by the stove drinking a glass of "hot stuff." They all struggled for the axe, and soon boarders came to the rescue. Finally, Harris said he would talk it over with Richards. This threw the rest off guard, and Harris quickly reached under the stairway, grabbed his shotgun, and blasted Richards in the heart. He pointed the gun at his wife, but bystanders wrenched it from his hands. Frustrated but still thinking, Harris reached down and grabbed the axe and with a final act of desperation smashed it against the face of Richards, now prostrate and moaning. Harris was then taken into custody, and most of the community sympathized with the murderer, who was an "honest, steady man, and well liked by everybody acquainted with him."[17]

Local government and politics were dominated by supervisory personnel from the mines. And, when judicial and legislative posts were available, company men were selected. The intent of this political activity was 100 per cent self-serving. Judges, legislators, prosecuting attorneys, and other officials did their best to protect the mining interests.

During the Civil War the Cliff managers worked so hard to dominate one election that their blatant maneuvers even startled the local newspaper. A caucus was held in Eagle River in March of 1863 to determine township officers. The

Cliff contingent did not show up, but they were still allotted some of the offices. But as they were not "the fattest of the lot" the Cliff officials called another caucus to be held at the mine, and there the entire slate were Cliff choices. A few days before the election, two barrels of beer were distributed, and many other promises were made.

On election day the mine closed, and all the workers were herded to the polls at the Odd Fellows Hall in Clifton. Two mining captains stationed themselves at either end of the ballot boxes. Yet, even these overt threats were not enough, because the Cliff opposition party won by a narrow margin. The key post was that of supervisor, and everyone wanted to control the position in order to influence taxation of the Cliff property.

The *Gazette* reporter was amazed that the Cliff closed down the mine and spent $3,000 "to elect a few petty officers." This was strange action at a time when copper prices were high and labor was scarce. But, the reporter concluded, the Cliff had such a desire to control everything that "they would stoop to almost any means to accomplish their object."[18]

Company dominance in political affairs was to continue for 100 years in the region. In 1870, for example, the three delegates to the Keweenaw County Republican Convention from Clifton were William H. Howe, Henry George, and John Penberthy, all Cliff supervisors, the latter two Cornishmen. Over the years John Forster, Sam Hill, and other mining officials mentioned in this book served the mineral interests well in the state capital and in Washington as legislators and congressmen. And in the twentieth century key local offices were usually held by the company men.[19]

The Civil War, as noted in an earlier chapter, had a tremendous impact on the mining villages. Hundreds of miners joined the Union Army, yet the companies were pressed to produce more copper than before. In Keweenaw County the villages quarreled over which was the most patriotic and which one sent the most men to join the Union Army. Eagle Harbor in August of 1863 set up an en-

William B. Wright, the main recruiter for Keweenaw County in the Civil War.

listment bounty of $50 for each single man, and ten at once signed up. The town claimed that nearby Eagle River was "determined to contribute neither men nor money." Copper Harbor was also criticized for being a nonpatriotic town. "To Eagle Harbor, therefore, belongs this glory of having furnished all the men and all the money in Keweenaw County."[20]

The race to prove patriotism was on. Captain Wright of Eagle Harbor and William H. Stevens of Copper Harbor took a cannon and four horses and went recruiting to Eagle River and the Cliff Mine. The cannon was fired, speeches made, and money raised. The meeting lasted for two days in the crowded quarters of the Odd Fellows Hall at Clifton. Most of the sessions consisted of individuals from the audience asking to be heard, so they could donate $20 or $50 to the fund. All the Cliff officials were on hand, as well as such area personalities as Dad Brockway, lawyer Jay Hubbell from Houghton. and J. Austrian, the leading businessman around. The crowd was in an emotional state, and

> everyone seemed to be endowed more or less with a military spirit. About 1500 people marched up and down the Cliff road in military style, headed by a fife and drum, a great number of whom wore the Garibaldi shirts.[21]

By the end of the festivities more than $5,000 was in the bounty fund, making Keweenaw County the leading county in the Upper Peninsula. In contrast to the previous article, the *Gazette* ended this account with HURRAH FOR KEWEENAW![22]

The effect of this public-spirited meeting on the recruiting drive is hard to estimate, but by early 1863 Keweenaw County boasted of having sent 92 men to fight the Rebels. The figure was bandied about because of another rivalry, this one between Keweenaw and Houghton counties.[23]

As the mining communities grew, some residents and the companies began to consider the amenities of church and school, When the copper lands were opened in the mid-1840s the only clergymen in the area were some forty miles to the south on Keweenaw Bay. Here a religious rivalry was warmly being carried on with the Methodist mission of Reverend John H. Pitezel on the east side of the bay and the Roman Catholic mission of Father Frederick Baraga on the western shore. Both missionaries were working with the local Chippewa tribe; the Methodists had been first on the scene, starting in the early 1830s.

Pitezel and Baraga made rigorous overland canoe and snowshoe trips to the new mining settlements. The missionaries were perplexed, because although their main task was to minister to the Indians, they saw that the hundreds of miners also needed spiritual guidance.[24] "Demon Rum" was king at Eagle River, and the new garrison at Fort Wilkins also needed clergymen's comfort.

In 1846 Pitezel made a chart showing religious conditions on Lake Superior. He preached "the first sermon ever" at the Cliff and Eagle River. Of the 122 inhabitants at the Cliff, 8 declared as Protestants and 3 as Catholics. With apathy like that, the clergyman's role would be tough. The pattern extended to other communities as well, for of the 27 inhabitants at Copper Harbor, 2 were Protestant and 4 were Catholic.[25] These figures are misleading because the young single males in the mining towns in the first years were not interested in "declaring" as anything, even though before—and later—many would be staunch Methodists.

Booze had to be fought, and in 1846 Pitezel delivered a temperance speech at the Cliff to a crowded and attentive audience. Thirty miners signed the pledge.[26] The Cliff officials encouraged Pitezel to settle there, and in November of 1847 he arrived to live in a crude log cabin provided by the company.

Evangelical efforts were handicapped by a communications gap, for Pitezel could not easily understand the Cornish dialect. Pitezel also knew that he was being "used" by the company:

> Many favored the institutions of religion as a matter of policy as connected with mining, who, so far as their own life and practice were concerned, lived in entire neglect of their spiritual interests.[27]

The churching results in the settlement were slim. "Some abandoned themselves to drinking and gambling, hunting and fishing, and other amusements on the Lord's day . . . . Vice and wickedness of various kinds and degrees obtained here a luxurious growth." For his church Pitezel used a small schoolroom abandoned the year before. He admitted that the services were not entirely satisfactory.

All was not pessimism though, for the residents were

respected for their frankness, warm and generous sympathy, liberality, and hospitality. Pitezel was amazed at the Cornish hymn singing ability, for the entire congregation sang, "and come nearest to our notion of the anthems of heaven of anything we can conceive."[28] Pitezel's talents and experience were needed on a wider front, and in 1848-1852 he served as head of all Methodist missions on Lake Superior. He was succeeded at Eagle River and the Cliff Mine by the Rev. Eri H. Day, a missionary who had also served with the Lake Superior Chippewas.[29]

Rev. Day arrived at the Cliff and was quartered in the coopers' building. The company also provided Day with $100 and the services of the company physician. His church was an old blacksmith shop fourteen feet square. Day found some old benches, a crude stove, and a small bell: the building then became his church and school. It was rude, hard work, and "when we had a dozen at church we had a large congregation."

Although clergymen were treated with respect, "men came to make money and everything must bend to that." Whiskey flowed, and fights were frequent, especially on Saturday nights. Men from several mines would get together, drink, and one would say "I am the best man." Another would answer, "Jemmy, I will try you." They would then strip to the waist, bets would be placed, and the fight was on.

Yet, Day would later recall that "these men were kind and generous." There were even gentlemen there. One, a draftsman at the Cliff, was a good artist and a good worker, but drinking killed him; "He was found frozen to death . . . with a bottle of whiskey by his side."

The second year at the mine was even worse for Rev. Day, as there were few men in the country who were not drinking. The Cliff mining captain was a heavy drinker, and he got tired of Day's temperance preachin' and kicked him out of camp. Day holed up at an abandoned house a few miles away and conducted school there. Day was happy indeed when the appointments list arrived: he was assigned to the Ontonagon range to the south. He would eventually

find that Cliff men were only men; it was the crude mining frontier that led to the practices of drinking and brawling.[30]

Time brought about many changes at the Cliff, and as the settlement became more permanent the men became less raucous. In the summer of 1849 Trowbridge, from the U.S. Mineral Land Office, reported that the miners had contributed $500 towards a new chapel, and that the foundation was already finished. He also reported that a good moral and religious influence existed, but this optimistic comment seems out of place after the bad reports given by ministers Pitezel and Day.[31]

Cornish Methodism has often been described as hot and loud praying, along with fervent hymn singing. The Reverend S. Steele in 1852 reported to Pitezel that attendance at the Cliff services was increasing steadily. On one Sabbath evening the exercises were so effective that

> under the preaching of the word, there was a general weeping all over the house, and the house was literally jammed to overflowing; several cried aloud for mercy, and one professed conversion at the time. Prayer meetings have been held nearly every night during the week, and several are converted.[32]

The Methodist report for 1865 described the Clifton church as a "commodious church, 65 x 35; a faithful Pastor, a successful Sabbath school, and general prosperity in morals and religion." Even after the Pittsburgh and Boston firm sold the Cliff property, the Methodist church was a community social-cultural center. In December of 1873 the Bath Brothers, assisted by members of Dad Brockway's family and others, gave a vocal and instrumental concert for the benefit of the church; in 1875 the nearby Phoenix Singers gave a concert for the benefit of local Methodism.[33] Near the turn of the century a storm hit the abandoned building and the roof fell in. A Finnish Methodist congregation from Laurium to the south salvaged much of the lumber and used it in their new church.[34]

One of the men who came to the Lake Superior country to regain his health was Hervey C. Parke, who joined his uncle Marquis Kelsey on the staff of the Cliff Mine. Parke

To the left is the Episcopal Church, and the tall structure near the center is the Methodist Church.

would go on to financial fame as founder of the pharmaceutical firm of Parke, Davis & Co., but during the years 1852-1863 he handled the business records for the Cliff property. In 1855 Parke and others planned an Episcopal congregation, and during the winter the church was built. It was consecrated in August of 1856 as Grace Episcopal Church. The first rector was the Rev. John Bramwell from England. Parke was the senior warden, Captain William Carnew junior warden, and other company officials held the other positions.[35]

Bramwell died in 1859, and some later rectors were William Long and William Johnston. By the mid-1860s the church was served by a rector from Central Mine, six miles to the north. The last services were held there in August of 1869. In 1872 the local Odd Fellows received permission to use the church as a lodge hall, and in 1909 the church was moved to Calumet.[36]

Most of the Germans and all of the Irish and French Canadians at Clifton were Roman Catholic. Father Baraga in the 1840s and other priests in later years periodically visited and said masses in the mining communities until 1854-55, when Holy Redeemer Church was built at Eagle Harbor. The large number of Catholics at Clifton and Eagle River asked for a church of their own, and in 1858 St. Marys Church was built there and was served by Father H. L. Thiele, the Eagle Harbor priest.[37]

In the mid-1860s Father Mathias Orth was at Clifton, apparently working hard and pleasing everyone, except a jealous neighborhood priest. Baraga, now a bishop, spent five days visiting the community, and his remarks about the Clifton priest are indicative of Orth's role in town:

> Where he resides, people of the three nations, Irish, French and Germans come with the same request, telling me that the three nations never harmonized so well in the Clifton Mission, as under his direction. He preaches every Sunday in English, French & German, and is night and day ready for services, without any partiality. He keeps no female servant in his house, but has a pious oldish man for his cook and sacristan.—Deo gratias![38]

Hervey Parke, founder of Parke, Davis and Company, who for years handled financial affairs at the Cliff. He was one of the founders of the Episcopal Church there.

Phoenix at the turn of the century. The Catholic Church in the foreground was moved from the Cliff, in the foothills to the left-center.

The Catholic church followed the fate of the two Protestant churches at Clifton. By the 1880s services were no longer held there. A mile or so to the north the settlement of Phoenix had a temporary mining spurt at the turn of the century, so the Clifton church was moved there in 1899 and was re-named Assumption Church. The church is still standing, in good repair, but is only infrequently used for religious services.[39]

The three churches meant much to the inhabitants of Clifton, but they were even more important to the managers of the Cliff Mine. The habits of drinking, fighting, and gambling were disruptive, and it was felt that a proper Christian atmosphere would soften the hard miners' characters. The company did more than merely encourage clergymen, they actually subsidized their efforts. For all three congregations the company donated land or provided clergymen's salaries.

Yet, in all the temperance sermons and hymn singing, a major fact seemed to be overlooked by company officials. The answer seems to be that problems decreased as the number of women increased. Family life led to a sense of permanence, of community life. The wild, drinking days of the 1840s were dominated by young, single men, whereas after the Cliff became the world's leading copper mine, people had the confidence to take their families to the village. True, from time to time some chronicler reported the absence of women as a negative characteristic, but no major company or religious policy was evolved that would change that circumstance. At any rate, the women gradually came, and they and the churches brought a sense of real community to Clifton.

From the earliest workings at the Cliff there had been a schoolroom, usually conducted by a minister or a priest. From 1848 on the company annual reports speak of a "schoolmaster" or "schoolroom," but these were often temporary, and from the memoirs of Rev. Eri H. Day and others we know that the facilities were crude, and books were not available. By 1860, though, a permanent school had been erected, and the annual report for the year claimed that "our school is in a flourishing condition having from 90 to 100 scholars in attendance."

A recently discovered diary kept by a teacher at Clifton during the Civil War gives us an excellent idea of the status of education and the degree of ethnic hostility common to the mining frontier. Henri Hobart, a Vermonter, came to the Cliff early in 1863 to teach 150 Cornish children, and a year later he wrote about Clifton as the "most God-forsaken place" in the country.[40]

Hobart became totally disgusted with Cornish people and gave as an example their celebration of July Fourth: "They are like hogs in every sense of the word . . . A crowd of whiskey soaked Beer Bellys are the blue-eyed set of Cornish." Some Cornish were "raving and under the influence of Gin," while others "abuse their wives and kick them and beat them." Hobart also pointed to habits such as dirty dishes, bread eaten off the floors, and so forth. He also disparaged the beauty of Cornish lasses:

> When I hear a young lady of 180 lbs. saying, Now here, he ain't good for noffing for such a brave one as she, Thee art a nice man etc., and this is not an uncommon display of the mental power of some, I am sick.

Though he despised his Cornish students and their par-

Lining up in Calumet to view the Grand Tournament, an annual Cornish affair. Families from Clifton, Central, Phoenix and other mining communities would always be on hand for such events.

ents, Hobart tried to improve their literacy by opening a night school for adults. Hobart was most ill at ease because he was not in the presence of "Americans," but was surrounded by Cornishmen, Irishmen, and Germans, all of whom looked upon water "as only fit for washing copper."

What amazed Hobart, but did not amaze other frontier observers, was that many of the characteristics he attributed to Cornishmen could be applied to people on any mining frontier. Cleanliness and tranquillity are not important in a mining camp, and if alcohol and hymn singing off-key lead to excitement and pleasure, so be it. The Cornish writer Todd calls Hobart a "sophisticated and insufferable prig," not a totally inaccurate evaluation. Schoolmaster Hobart claimed the Cornishmen cared not for this country so did not rally to the colors in the Civil War; Todd writes that Hobart "shows no haste to throw away his chalks and enlist."

The population of Clifton declined rapidly in the late 1860s, and in the 1870 report by the county superintendent of schools it is clear that Keweenaw County boom times are over. Of all the villages, only in Eagle Harbor were books purchased in that year. The volumes in the libraries number 504 in Clifton, 608 in Eagle Harbor, 480 in Copper Harbor. New equipment ordered for the schools included alphabet cards, reading cards, numeral frames, dictionaries, globes, wall maps, and a new blackboard.[41] By 1875 Clifton's population was below 500, but a school was maintained there through the 1880s.[42]

The story of a community is not merely a chronicle of schools, churches, and politics, but it must also be a story of the inhabitants. One of these was John Gundry, born in Cornwall, who came to the Cliff in 1851 and was soon chief mining captain. He was responsible for many of the machine improvements in the following decade. In 1863-64 he moved south to the Portage Lake district, serving as chief captain at the Pewabic Mine. When Gundry died of cancer in 1864 the *Mining Gazette* published an obituary that must rank as the most ridiculous, most hilarious, or most poignant ever published for a miner. It reads in part:

Life is, at most, but an "eight hour shift," in which we labor for an eternal recompense, and be the ground hard or soft we shall be paid at the office above according to the rate we have worked.

The great Superintendent of all things, has "rung down the shaft," extending from heaven to earth, "for Capt. John to come up." And obedient to the summons, he gave his last orders, and started up the ladder, the flickering candle of his life growing shorter and shorter as he neared the surface. Just as it went out, he stepped up through the "man-hole" into the bright, clear light of eternity, and the eyes of his spirit took in the boundless space of the "brighter world." No more groping in earthly darkness, no more straining of eyesight to penetrate the surrounding gloom; it is all plain now; the dark corners are illuminated; the great mystery, that has ever baffled human knowledge, is solved![43]

A real success story is that of J. W. Rawlins, inventor of North America's first "Man-Engine." Rawlins was born in Camborne, Cornwall, in 1826. Both his parents died while he was young, so Rawlins was raised by relatives. At fourteen he quit school to become a machinist at a nearby mine. A few years later he worked with his cousin Nicholas Vivian, designing an engine for the Bruce copper mines in Ontario.[44]

In 1850 Rawlins went to the New World and reached Eagle River in June. He went to the Cliff Mine, where in good Cornish fashion "I was well received by my cousin Nicholas Vivian." Rawlins worked as an engineer at the Cliff and other nearby mines until 1853, when he went to the Minesota Mine to the south. Disappointed with conditions there, he returned to the Cliff and was offered the position of mechanical engineer. He at once found a good boarding house kept by a widow with a few children. "We got along so well together that I finally married her."

A mine captain who objected to Rawlins' smoking on the grounds ordered him to quit smoking or leave. After a few days Rawlins announced he was leaving, but the captain was perplexed. Wages bad? Poor working conditions? Have a better job? Rawlins answered no to all these questions, saying he was leaving rather than give up smoking.

After a trip to some other mines for a few days Rawlins returned and was escorted into an office by the mine agent. It was a new office, especially made for Rawlins, and there was also a tin of tobacco and half a dozen new pipes. Rawlins "drop'd into the chair and cried my heart out almost." He was given charge of all the machinery in the mine, and the management only asked that he not smoke in front of the men.

Once Rawlins was involved in a "chain of command" argument that helps explain Cornish mining mentality. A mining captain wandered by and told Ned Richards, an employee of Rawlins, to start an engine. Ned said he could only do so on proper authority, meaning that of Rawlins. The captain "call'd Ned all the filth he could call to mind" and fired him. The agent of the mine backed the captain, so at the end of the month Rawlins packed his gear and boarded the stage, "for it that was to be the future method, the sooner I got a new chance the better." The mine agent stopped the stage and demanded an explanation. Rawlins told him Ned was a prince of a fellow and a great worker and that the mine captain was foul-mouthed; supposedly, only Rawlins could hire or fire men working on machinery. "Now good bye sir, and thank you for the happiest place I ever had." The agent at once apologized for acting without talking to Rawlins, and he persuaded Rawlins to stay on and hire as many Neds as he wanted.

An incident mentioned in Rawlins' memoirs involves the Cornish love for loud music. A professor of music from Boston was visiting the mine agent and was amazed when he heard the band playing so well. He sent for the band leader, Isaac Blank, whose clothes were still dripping with muddy mine water. The Boston gent politely demanded to know how Blank knew so much music without being educated.

Blank explained that he was raised in a small village in Cornwall and never went to school. When he grew up he learned to play the clarinet, and when the teacher died Blank became leader of the village band. "Times growing

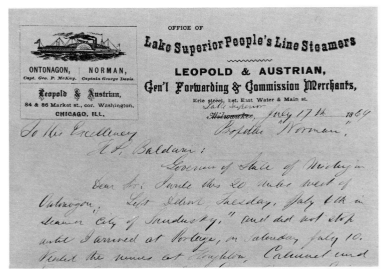

Leopold and Austrian maintained merchant houses in several Lake Superior ports, including Eagle River.

bad, I came to this place and soon started the band." How could Blank play so well without being able to read music? "When hearing music play'd by a good player, he observed the characters written here and there on the pages, was the key to the situation."

When Cliff production declined, Rawlins went to the Houghton-Hancock area, where he became a respected engineer-designer of mining equipment. He wrote his memoirs in 1914 when he was eighty-eight.

A few miles away from the Cliff was the port of Eagle River, from which all the local copper was shipped. The town was started in 1845 because of the workings of the Lake Superior Company, but once the Cliff became successful, Eagle River's fortunes were tied to that mine. By 1846 the village had a sawmill, a few roads, over a hundred residents, and "the appearance of a thriving village."[45] Schools and missions were soon started, and to prove that the town was on the way to cultural advance, the residents in 1851 invited Mr. Robinson to visit there and set up his "Daguerrean Room" where they could "get perfect likenesses of themselves."[46]

Eagle River had a series of docks over the years—all of them bad. The combination of lake storms and shallow water meant continual repairs to port facilities.

Eagle River was mostly settled by Germans, and even the Methodists set up a special German mission there to look after them. In 1852 the congregation numbered 50, and the Sunday school had 63 scholars and a library of 150 volumes.[47]

By the mid-1850s the town had hundreds of residents and big plans, largely because of the Cliff production, but also because the best land at the end of the river was made available for purchase by the Phoenix Mining Company. The Phoenix agent at the time was Sam Hill. In 1855 the land for the town of Eagle River was surveyed and platted, and a temporary building boom was on.[48]

As a port Eagle River was terrible. The beach was shallow, and there was no major indentation on the Lake Superior shoreline near the town. Over the years the only way to load and unload was either to move goods from craft to craft or to build piers out into the lake. By 1853 the firm of Senter & Mandlebaum had a pier of 700 feet extending into the lake, but if the savage winds and waves of Lake Superior did not crush the pier, most observers felt that the winter ice would.[49]

The entire coast of Lake Superior was a shipping nightmare for even the most experienced of pilots. A string of lighthouses was soon built; Copper Harbor in 1849, Eagle Harbor in 1851, Eagle River in 1858. This last light was south-west of town, a few miles from the Cliff Mine. The beacon was to shine from here until 1908, but even so the Lake Superior furies caused many accidents along this coast.

One of the numerous shipping problems occurred in November of 1864 when Von Siebold, the postmaster and town jeweler, was going in a yawl to the "Ironsides" to transfer mail. Furious winds whipped up and sent him and his boat out to sea. The "Ironsides" sent a small boat after him, but that, too, was taken away. The "Ironsides" then went after both boats, but just as she was gaining ground on Von Siebold, her engines broke down. After a few minutes, the crew watched Von Siebold bob away in the distance, never to be seen again.[50]

A "great conflagration" struck Eagle River in 1867, destroying the entire business section.[51] This was the first of the many village fires on Lake Superior; almost every community would have such a disaster before the turn of the century. By this time, though, Eagle River was declining as a port of consequence, because Cliff production was falling rapidly. One later account stated that with the closing of the Cliff, the business of Eagle River "folded its tents, like the Arabs, and silently stole away."[52]

Clifton, Central Mine, Copper Harbor, Copper Falls, and other early towns were primarily Cornish, especially the mining population, though some Irish and Germans also did the menial or unskilled jobs in the mines. In this early period few Cornishmen took an interest in business, and most of the stores and transportation outfits on the peninsula were handled by "Americans," Germans, or German Jews.

The population of Clifton varied greatly over the years, but the ethnic ratio remained fairly constant. Statistics for Clifton Township for 1870 show a fine breakdown for foreign-born residents:

England	172	Canada	11
Germany	86	Switzerland	4
Ireland	53		

Seat of justice and jail for rowdy miners—Keweenaw County buildings in Eagle River.

These are figures that omit the 282 "American" born, because more than 75 per cent of them were children of the above-listed ethnic groups. England, of course, meant Cornwall; there was no "Germany" listed in the census, but specific principalities such as Saxony, Bavaria, and Wurtemburg were given. By Canada was usually meant French Canada.[53]

The only meaningful ethnic change for the few decades was a decline in number of French Canadians. These people could be found in every town, and in every forest, but it was almost impossible to find a French Canadian working in a mine. Instead, they often made up the bulk of the surface crews; especially were they fond of providing timber, horse transportation, and fuel wood. By the time of the 1870 census Clifton provided little opportunity for these skills. When the great firm of Calumet & Hecla founded stamp mills at Lake Linden in the 1860s, Joseph Gregoire persuaded hundreds of his Quebec compatriots to settle around Lake Linden, but again they came as lumberjacks and teamsters, not as miners. Later, they did take up work in the stamping mills and smelters, but French Canadians continued to look upon mining as something unnatural.[54]

1. The ramifications of the new leasing system can be seen in the *Niles' National Register;* July 15 and August 26, 1843. In the issue of *Niles'* for July 29, 1843, the opening lines of one article exclaimed that "We were not a little astonished" to learn that John D. Ansly obtained from the federal government a permit for 27 sections of Lake Superior land. A lengthy letter from Porter to Cunningham, April 13, 1843, explaining the new leasing policies, is printed in Fadner, *Fort Wilkins and the U.S. Mineral Land Agency*, pp. 156-59.

2. A. L. Rowse, *The Cousin Jacks: The Cornish in America* (New York: Charles Scribner's Sons, 1969), p. 169, and Arthur Cecil Todd, *The Cornish Miner in America* (Glendale, Calif.: Arthur H. Clark Co., 1967), chapter 4. See also January 2, 1908, clipping "Early Life in the Copper Country," in the Brockway Papers, University of Michigan Historical Collections, Ann Arbor.

3. Gates, *Michigan Copper and Boston Dollars*, p. 103; *Mining Magazine*, I (1853), 295.

4. Several Hays obituaries are in the Brockway Papers.

5. Most annual reports mention the physician, his quarters, etc. The best summary of medical care is in Gates, *Michigan Copper and Boston Dollars*, pp. 103-04.

6. Day's autobiographical sketch is in *Michigan Pioneer Collections*, XIV (1890).

7. Vivian's article, "Cornwall Gives Legacy to Area Mining," appeared in the *Daily Mining Gazette* (Houghton), June 13, 1970.

8. *Annual Report, Pittsburgh & Boston Mining Company, 1849*, pp. 9-10.

9. Issue of May 14, 1851.

10. *Mining Magazine*, VII (1856), 311.

11. *Annual Report, Pittsburgh & Boston Mining Company, 1860*, p. 21.

12. Hays obituaries, Brockway Papers.

13. Gates, *Michigan Copper and Boston Dollars*, p. 104.

14. *Mining Gazette* (Houghton), January 31, 1863.

15. The Ontonagon "battle" is reported in the *Detroit Free Press*, May 10, 1859. For the Hancock affair see *Mining Gazette* (Houghton), January 17, 1863.

16. *Mining Gazette* (Houghton), January 10, January 24, 1863.

17. Account of the murder is in *ibid.*, December 13, 1863.

18. *Ibid.*, April 25, 1863.

19. I noticed this circumstance in much detail when I wrote a history of my hometown, *Hubbell: A Copper Country Village* (Lansing: the author, 1969), pp. 17-22.

20. *Mining Gazette* (Houghton), August 16, 1862.

21. Detailed accounts in *ibid.*, August 30 and September 6, 1862.

22. *Ibid.*, August 23, 1862. A later account of this affair appeared in the *Keweenaw Miner*, March 11, 1916.

23. *Mining Gazette* (Houghton), February 14, 1863.

24. A good summary of the situation is by Bernard Lambert, "Mission Priorities: Indians or Miners?" *Michigan History*, LI (Winter, 1967), 323-34.

25. John H. Pitezel, *Lights and Shades of Missionary Life* (Cincinnati: Western Book Concern, 1859), p. 141, Table 1.

26. *Ibid.*, p. 143.

27. *Ibid.*, p. 158.

28. *Ibid.*, pp. 162-63.

29. See "Role of Missionaries" in *ibid.*, pp. 466-67.

30. Day, *Michigan Pioneer Collections*, XIV (1890), 205-56.

31. Account appears in Michigan, *Joint Documents* (1850), p. 56.

32. Pitezel, *Lights and Shades*, pp. 369-71.

33. *Portage Lake Mining Gazette* (Houghton), February 18, 1865; December 11, 1873; May 27, 1875.

34. *Daily Mining Gazette* (Houghton), September 2, 1955.

35. I wrote a summary of Parke's mining career in *ibid.*, April 5, 1969. For a history of the church see a clipping in the Brockway Scrapbook, p. 63.

36. *Hancock Evening Journal*, December 18, December 23, 1908. For this, and much of the religious information about Clifton, I received much help from Miss Barbara Williams of Evanston, Illinois, formerly librarian in Calumet, Mich.

37. Antoine Rezek, *History of the Diocese of Sault Ste. Marie and Marquette* (Chicago: M. A. Donahue & Co., 1906), I, 83-84, II, 297-98.

38. Baraga to Archbishop Purcell of Cincinnati, June 15, 1866, copy in the Baraga Papers, Michigan Historical Commission, Lansing.

39. *Daily Mining Gazette* (Houghton), August 22, 1953; August 6, 1966.

40. For the remarks about Hobart I am following Todd, *Cornish Miner in America*, pp. 119-25.

41. *Michigan School Reports* (1870), p. 84.

42. *Michigan State Gazeteer* (Detroit: R. L, Polk & Co., 1883), p. 400, mentions a "graded school" at Clifton.

43. *Portage Lake Mining Gazette* (Houghton), October 15, 1864.

44. The Rawlins information is from his "Recollections of a Long Life," which appeared in *Copper Country Tales, Volume I* (Calumet: Roy W. Drier, 1967), pp. 75-119.

45. *Lake Superior News and Miners' Journal* (Copper Harbor), August 29, 1846.

46. *Lake Superior Journal* (Sault Ste. Marie), June 11, 1851.

47. Pitezel, *Lights and Shades*, p. 369.

48. *Lake Superior Journal* (Sault Ste. Marie), September 24, 1853. The

plat is in the Records of the Auditor General, Michigan State Archives, Lansing.

49. *Lake Superior Journal* (Sault Ste. Marie), September 17, 1853.
50. *Portage Lake Mining Gazette* (Houghton), November 12, 1864.
51. *Ibid.*, June 27, 1867.
52. *Ibid.*, September 18, 1873.

53. The original population census for Keeweenaw County, 1870, is in the Michigan State Archives, Lansing.
54. Detailed evidence of this French-Canadian attitude appears in my *Hubbell: A Copper Country Village*. Lake Linden and Hubbell are neighboring towns on Torch Lake, settled primarily by French Canadians.

Chapter 6:

The Later Years

WHEN THE CLIFF PROPERTY was written off in December of 1871 by the Pittsburgh and Boston Company, a few Boston financiers headed by Marshall H. Simpson felt strongly enough to buy all the company holdings in the county for $100,000. The choice to lead the Cliff back to super production was Oliver A. Farwell of Boston, who since the 1850s had been associated with the nearby Phoenix Mining Company. Farwell arrived at Clifton before the end of 1871 and pessimistically took stock of the situation. He even considered having the Cliff worked "on tribute," but soon discarded the idea. Tribute was a system in which a firm allowed a group of men to come in and work the property; the company took a share of the profits. Copper expert Horace J. Stevens called tribute "a form of grand larceny, at the expense of the mine's future." Tributors, of course, were only interested in immediate gains, so they avoided doing necessary timbering, testing, and so forth.[1]

During all of 1872 and part of the next year Farwell had a crew of around 200, mostly working at pumping out the mine. By late 1873 the Cliff was back in production, and some mass copper was found. From time to time the old optimism was repeated, as a 500 pound mass or so would be found. Yet, from 1874 to 1879 the work force dwindled from 250 to 50. No glowing reports could offset the meaning of the employment decline.[2]

The fact was that the Cliff was one of the lowest producers in the county. For example, in 1871 when the Cliff shipped 90 tons, the Central shipped 905 and the Phoenix 879. Yet, even these respectable figures were overshadowed by the new colossus a few miles to the south: the Calumet & Hecla Company, working the new conglomerate fields, mined 9,660 tons![3]

New activity at the Cliff, even though it lacked the vigor and success of earlier years, meant at least a temporary spurt for the nearby port of Eagle River. One energetic news account in 1873 by "Waif-airer" claimed that the Cliff had caused Eagle River to "come forth again to light and life." Former merchants were opening their doors, new merchants were coming to town, and the Wright Hotel business was thriving. And at Clifton, D. D. Brockway

("Doctor of Divinity, Dead for a Ducat . . . Vichever you please") was doing a brisk business at his general store. "I just hear that a 40 ton mass is 'cutting up' at the Cliff. There's life in the old dog yet."[4]

By the mid-1870s the Cliff was said usually to be "still promising" or "looking well," and the copper mined did increase a bit, from 157 tons in 1872 to 824 tons in 1875.[5] But the number of men on the payroll decreased, as the mass copper gave out. The *Mining Gazette* said kind words about the company in 1877 because of their concern for "fissure" copper deposits of Lake Superior. The newspaper cautioned against concluding that fewer men meant less copper. They advocated waiting for new developments which would give the old Cliff "a new lease of life."[6]

These hopeful statements were not shared by the management, for in the spring of 1879 the Cliff, all buildings and machinery, and 3,500 acres were offered for sale through agent Farwell. Things had gone so badly by this time that Farwell had worked out a deal with thirty men to work the mine on tribute.[7]

No great financier stepped forward to buy the Cliff, so Farwell stayed on and had a few men working on tribute until his death at Clifton in June of 1881. His death meant a lot to the little community, for he was well liked, and he enjoyed talking with people about his visits in Europe, Asia, and South America. The Farwell family by this time had permanent roots in the Keweenaw country, so they stayed on in the agent's house. Farwell's daughters Bessie and Jessie taught school at Phoenix and Clifton.[8]

Daniel "Dad" Brockway dominated the decade of the 1880s at the Cliff, though *dominate* is perhaps too strong a word. He became agent after the death of Farwell, and at the same time continued to run the nearby Atlas Mine, a small producer. After a few years as blacksmith at the L'Anse Chippewa reservation, Brockway in 1846 had moved to Copper Harbor where he opened a hotel. During the next thirty years he operated stores in several Keweenaw County villages, served as agent for some of the smaller mines, was a road commissioner, and eventually came in

VALUABLE MINING PROPERTY.

Cliff Copper Mine

FOR SALE.

THE PROPERTY KNOWN AS THE

CLIFF MINE

Situated in the center of the copper-bearing mineral range of

Keweenaw Point, on Lake Superior,

COMPRISING ALL THE

Buildings and Machinery on said Mine and about 3,500 Acres of Land,

on which is the famous CLIFF VEIN, is now offered for sale.

"Dad" Brockway and wife Lucena.

Eagle River; the front buildings were boarding houses for miners.

contact with most people and organizations on the peninsula. He was chosen agent at the Cliff not because of his
great mining talents, but because he knew the community
well, he was admired by everyone, and he had had some
experience.[9]

The Brockway family also had a meaningful marriage
tie here, as Dan's daughter Charlotte had married Oliver
Farwell, previous Cliff agent. As early as 1874 Brockway's
role in peninsula history was known to all, as he was one of
those featured in an "Old Settlers Party" in Eagle River. In
1886 Dan and wife Lucena became the first couple in the
Copper Country to celebrate a golden wedding anniversary, and a gala affair was held in their honor at the Calumet
armory.[10]

The mining at the Cliff continued, but only as a ghost of
the past. Production in 1883 was 38 tons, compared to 901
tons at the Central. Brockway went to Boston the following year to confer with the mine owners, and during his absence the work was suspended. When fire destroyed Brockway's barn in 1884 and killed two horses, it was a major
disaster for this once-famous outfit.[11]

Nostalgia and mostly pessimism were all that the Michigan Commissioner of Mineral Statistics could offer for the
Cliff in 1886. Commissioner Charles Lawton wrote of the
"romantic interest" once attached to the now-idle mine
and theorized that the Cliff just ran into too much poor
ground. "People will scarcely cease to conjecture as to
what might be the result if it were again worked as of old."

LONGITUDINAL SECTION OF THE CLIFF MINE, 1881.

Scale, 600 ft. to one inch.

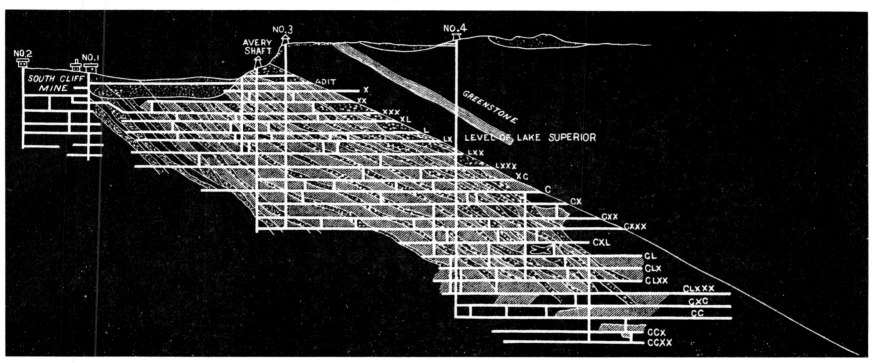

By this date, all that was impressive about the Cliff was its depth.

LONGITUDINAL SECTION OF THE MINESOTA MINE.

Scale, 300 ft. to one inch.

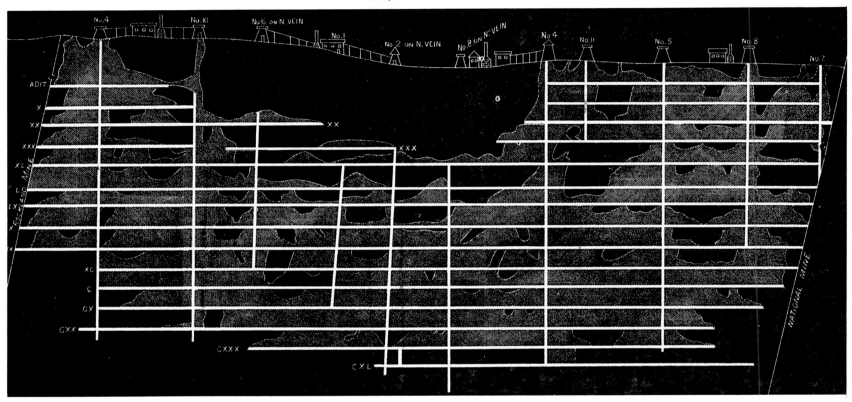

By 1881 the Minesota, too, was exhausted.

Brockway was still in charge of the grounds and equipment, though the works had ceased operations. Even in the 1890s Brockway was searching for copper, using such modern equipment as diamond drills. In all, over 2,600 feet of strata were explored, but nothing was found to justify reopening the mine.[12]

Mild interest was shown in the North Cliff property in 1899 by a group of Boston financiers, and they even dragged James Sowden, retired Cliff mining captain, from his rocking chair to declare that the North Cliff "has the appearance of the old Cliff." These were mere dreams, for the Keweenaw copper mines were tired. By 1903 only the Mohawk was producing copper.[13]

A no-return decision was made in 1903, as the owners of the Cliff property stripped the shaft house, engine house, and stamp mill and sent the machinery to Houghton where it was sold for scrap iron. The Cliff Mining Company continued to exist, but the stock was now controlled by board members of the fabulously wealthy Calumet & Hecla firm. In 1912 R. L. Agassiz was president of both firms.[14] Agassiz was also president in 1918, but a geological report of that time listed the Cliff Mining Company as a "Subsidiary of Calumet & Hecla Mining Co."[15]

Many crosscuts, drifts, and other exploratory workings were done at the Cliff in the twentieth century, but none of them led to reopening of the mine. The last mine buildings were scrapped, and all houses, barns, and stores in the village were demolished. Today one could drive along the road a few feet from this once world-famous mine and see only a majestic tree-covered cliff, a few rock piles, and a bronze plaque on a boulder honoring discoverer John Hays. The Cliff is dead.

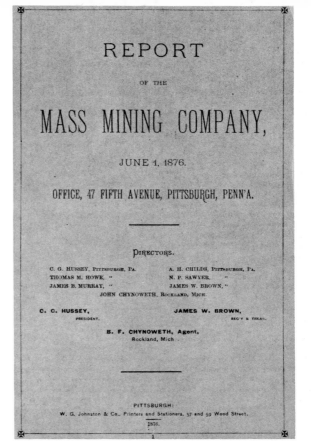

Hussey and Howe gave up on the Cliff, but they retained interests in several mines on the Ontonagon range.

The gazetteer entry for 1883 is not flattering.

CLIFTON. A village of 350 inhabitants, in Clifton township, Keweenaw county, four miles back from Eagle River, the county seat. It is the location of the famous Cliff mine, which is 1,080 feet deep, and of the stamp mills of the company. The surface of the country is hilly and rocky; soil sandy and productive of vegetables, hay, oats and barley. There are two churches, Methodist and Catholic, and a graded school. Copper is the only shipment. Improved land, $20 per acre. Calumet, on the M. R. R., 12 miles distant, is the nearest railroad station, to which and Eagle River a mail stage runs daily, fares $1.00 and 50 cents respectively. Telegraph, W. U. J. C. Trenbath, postmaster.

Brockway D D, agent Cliff Copper Co.
Cliff Copper Co, copper mines.
Lawbaugh A J, physician.
Trenbath J C, Clerk Copper Co and Justice.
Wilson George, justice of peace.
Witcomb Rev (Methodist Episcopal.)

Clifton, exhausted and abandoned.

1. For change in ownership, see Michigan, *Annual Report, Commissioner of Mineral Statistics, 1880*, pp. 19-20; for Farwell's arrival see *Portage Lake Mining Gazette*, December 14 and December 21, 1871; for tribute definition see Horace J. Stevens (ed.), *Copper Handbook*, VIII (1908), 165.

2. Employment figures from *Annual Report, Commissioner of Mineral Statistics, 1880*, p. 19; for an example of temporary optimism, see *Portage Lake Mining Gazette*, October 30, 1873.

3. *Portage Lake Mining Gazette*, December 14, 1871.

4. This letter, crammed with good Eagle River information, is in the *Portage Lake Mining Gazette*, September 18, 1873.

5. *Ibid.*, April 13, 1876.

6. *Ibid.*, April 26, 1877.

7. *Ibid.*, May 1, 1879 (advertisement); July 3, 1879.

8. Obituary and other family information in *ibid.*, June 30, August 11, 1881. Farwell died of cancer on June 22 at age seventy.

9. Summarized from the Brockway Papers, University of Michigan Historical Collections.

10. For Charlotte's marriage see Brockway Scrapbook, p. 5; for "Old Settlers" see *Portage Lake Mining Gazette*, March 12, 1874; anniversary article in *Calumet News*, January 23, 1886.

11. For 1882 production see *Portage Lake Mining Gazette*, January 11, 1883; for trip to Boston see *ibid.*, March 8, 1883; for fire article, *ibid.*, September 4, 1884.

12. Michigan, *Mineral Resources, 1885* (Lansing: Thorp & Godfrey, 1886), p. 231; C. Rominger, *Geological Report of the Upper Peninsula of Michigan* (Lansing: State Printer, 1895), pp. 122-24.

13. *Michigan Miner*, I (March 1, 1899), 26: *Mining Journal* (Marquette), May 23, 1903.

14. *Mining Journal* (Marquette), May 2, 1903; *Mineral Resources of Michigan* (Lansing: Wynkoop, Hallenbeck, Crawford Co., 1913), p. 27.

15. R. C. Allen, *Mineral Resources of Michigan, 1918* (Lansing: Geological and Biological Survey, 1918), p. 24.

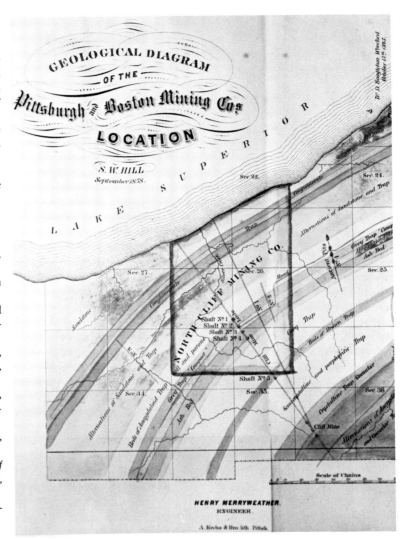

Eagle River in relation to various Cliff mines.

In the 1890's the Central, the last large mass mine in Keweenaw, stopped production.

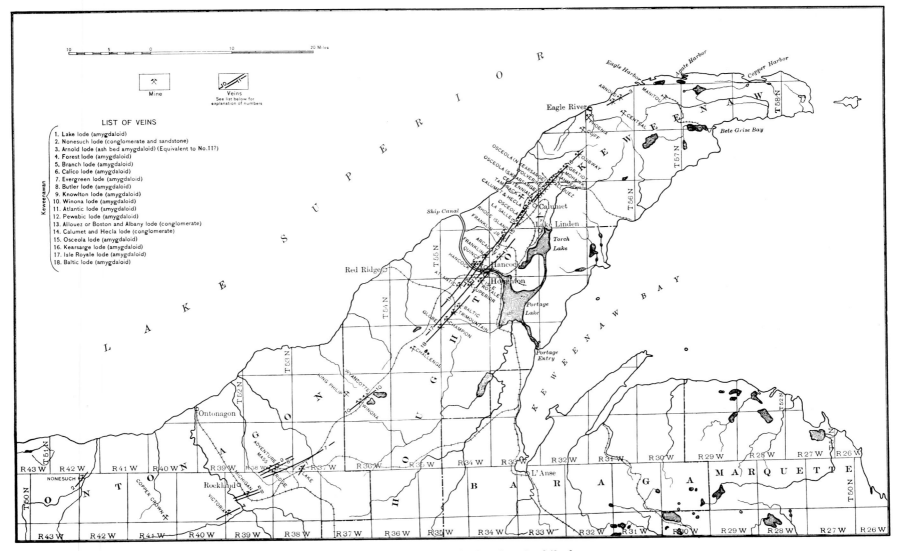

LIST OF VEINS

1. Lake lode (amygdaloid)
2. Nonesuch lode (conglomerate and sandstone)
3. Arnold lode (ash bed amygdaloid) (Equivalent to No.11?)
4. Forest lode (amygdaloid)
5. Branch lode (amygdaloid)
6. Calico lode (amygdaloid)
7. Evergreen lode (amygdaloid)
8. Butler lode (amygdaloid)
9. Knowlton lode (amygdaloid)
10. Winona lode (amygdaloid)
11. Atlantic lode (amygdaloid)
12. Pewabic lode (amygdaloid)
13. Allouez or Boston and Albany lode (conglomerate)
14. Calumet and Hecla lode (conglomerate)
15. Osceola lode (amygdaloid)
16. Kearsarge lode (amygdaloid)
17. Isle Royale lode (amygdaloid)
18. Baltic lode (amygdaloid)

By the turn of the century the mass mines of Keweenaw and Ontonagon were practically abandoned, while the mines of Houghton County were among the world's leaders in production.

All that remains of Clifton today—rugged beauty and rock piles.

LIST OF MINING TERMS

This is not a technical study, but some of the terminology might be vague or unknown to readers. The following definitions of terms used in this book are adapted from Horace Stevens, *Copper Handbook*, VIII (1908).

Adit A horizontal mine opening driven into a hill or mountain.

Amygdaloid Igneous rocks which in the Lake Superior region often contain metal in the amygdules—almond-shaped cavities.

Bal Cornish word for mine.

Conglomerate A pudding-stone rock which in the Lake Superior district is often cemented together with pure copper.

Drift A horizontal opening in a mine; *adit* is the term usually applied only to the initial opening.

Float copper Pure copper carried far from its original site by glaciers.

Greenstone Diorite; a granular, igneous rock.

Kibble Cornish word for metal bucket used to raise copper from mine.

Man Engine A Cornish device for raising and lowering miners in deep-shaft mines.

Mass A solid chunk of native copper.

Native Copper A virgin metal; not an ore.

Shaft A downward mine opening having its upper end at surface.

Stamps Machines to crush rock or ore by heavy blows.
Stope The excavation above a drift.

Whim A windlass with a horizontal drum, devised by Cornish miners for raising and lowering kibbles.

Winze A Cornish term for a steeply inclined passageway to connect two different working levels.

The beginning place for mining research should be company annual reports, for although these are usually optimistic, the production and dividend statistics are not padded. The published reports are scattered in various libraries and archives across the country. Many were published in full in the Houghton *Portage Lake Mining Gazette* and other newspapers. Hundreds of manuscript annual reports and articles of incorporation are chronologically arranged in the State Archives, Michigan Historical Commission, Lansing.

The State Archives also has an excellent collection of other manuscript material, along with the Victor F. Lemmer Collection, which contains a variety of published works: government documents, maps, trade journals, reminiscences, and travel narratives.

Several hundred mining accounts can be found in the *Michigan Pioneer Collections* (40 vols.) and *Michigan History*, a quarterly established by the Michigan Historical Commission in 1917. An excellent series of articles by Robert Hybels on the opening of the copper region appeared in *Michigan History* in 1950. Another useful work is the *Proceedings of the Lake Superior Mining Institute*. This organization, started in the 1890s, published from three to six articles in each year's *Proceedings*.

For this study I also used the rich mining, steel industry, and biographical materials of the Pennsylvania Room, Carnegie Library, Pittsburgh, and the University of Michigan Historical Collections, Ann Arbor, which has the Daniel Brockway Papers. The Michigan State Library, Lansing, has a good collection of nineteenth century periodicals. Particularly useful for this study were *Niles' National Register*, *Harper's Monthly*, and *Western Magazine of History*. The State Library also has an extensive collection of newspapers on microfilm. Almost every issue of the following contain mining information: *Lake Superior News and Miners' Journal* (Copper Harbor, later Sault Ste. Marie), *Portage Lake Mining Gazette* (Houghton), and the *Mining Journal* (Marquette).

Few books have been written about Lake Superior copper mining. Of these the most scholarly is William B. Gates, Jr., *Michigan Copper and Boston Dollars* (Cambridge: Harvard University Press, 1951). This is thoroughly documented and places the Lake Superior scene in its proper national perspective: C. H. Benedict's *Red Metal: The Calumet & Hecla Story* (Ann Arbor: University of Michigan Press, 1952) is an undocumented narrative by a metallurgist who had much to do with that firm's success. Angus Murdoch's *Boom Copper: The Story of the First United States Mining Boom* (New York: Macmillan Co., 1943) is a folksy approach to an understanding of the region. Based on fairly sound research, *Boom Copper* remains one of the most interesting local history studies of the Midwest.

PICTURE CREDITS

THE MAJORITY of the illustrations used in this book came from the rich collections of the Michigan Historical Commission, Lansing. Many of the illustrations, including some of those from published works, are from the Marquette County Historical Society, the Michigan State Library, and the Pennsylvania Room, Carnegie Library, Pittsburgh. The personnel at these institutions extended their fullest cooperation during my visits, and I wish to thank them for filling my every request.

INDEX

2500 copies
Printed at Sequoia Press
Kalamazoo, Michigan
December 1971.
Set in Baskerville
on the AM 725 phototypesetting
system.

FIRST EDITION